better
transportation
for
your city

a Guide to the Factual Development of Urban Transportation Plans

NATIONAL COMMITTEE ON URBAN TRANSPORTATION

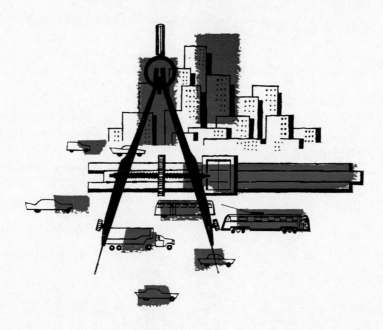

PUBLIC ADMINISTRATION SERVICE

1313 EAST 60TH STREET, CHICAGO 37, ILLINOIS

NATIONAL COMMITTEE ON URBAN TRANSPORTATION

1346 CONNECTICUT AVENUE, NORTH WEST, WASHINGTON 6, D. C.

chairman GLENN C. RICHARDS
Commissioner of Public Works, Detroit, Michigan
Representing American Public Works Association

vice chairman HON. BEN WEST
Mayor of Nashville, Tennessee
Representing American Municipal Association

members O. W. CAMPBELL
County Manager, Dade County, Florida
Representing International City Managers' Association

JOSEPH H. CROWLEY
Director of Law, Cleveland, Ohio, Representing
National Institute of Municipal Law Officers

E. H. HOLMES
Deputy Commissioner, U. S. Bureau of Public Roads
Representing Bureau of Public Roads, Washington, D. C.

JAMES M. LISTER
Director of Urban Renewal & Housing, Cleveland, Ohio
Representing American Society of Planning Officials

JOSEPH J. MITCHELL
City Comptroller, St. Paul, Minnesota
Representing Municipal Finance Officers Association

GEORGE S. MOONEY
Executive Director, Canadian Federation of Mayors
and Municipalities, Montreal, Quebec

DONALD C. SCRIBNER
Treasurer, Fulton County, New York
Representing National Association of County Officials

secretary ORIN F. NOLTING
Executive Director
International City Managers' Association

treasurer JOSEPH F. CLARK
Executive Director
Municipal Finance Officers Association of the
United States and Canada

285571

consultants to the **NATIONAL COMMITTEE ON URBAN TRANSPORTATION**

WALTER BLUCHER, Consultant
American Society of Planning Officials

G. DONALD KENNEDY, Chairman
Highway Research Board, 1954-55

D. GRANT MICKLE, Director
Traffic Engineering Division
Automotive Safety Foundation

RALPH R. BARTELSMEYER, Chief Highway Engineer
Illinois Division of Highways
Representing American Association of State Highway Officials

WILFRED OWEN, Senior Staff Member
Brookings Institution

OSCAR SUTERMEISTER, Consultant
Urban Evacuation Study
The Johns Hopkins University

GEORGE W. ANDERSON, Vice President
American Transit Association

NORMAN KENNEDY, Assistant Director
Institute of Transportation and Traffic Engineering
University of California

staff director W. A. RUSCH

consultant to ALAN M. VOORHEES
the staff director Automotive Safety Foundation

editorial consultant ALBERT PROCTOR
Automotive Safety Foundation

assistant to JACK BERMAN
the staff director

SUBCOMMITTEES

Administration

RAY W. WILSON, *Chairman*
City Manager, Phoenix, Arizona

WILLIAM E. BILLINGS
Executive Vice President and
Secretary, Cleveland Safety
Council, Cleveland, Ohio

MILTON BREIVOGEL
Director of Planning
Regional Planning Commission
Los Angeles County, California

L. P. COOKINGHAM
City Manager, Kansas City, Missouri

HONORABLE deLESSEPS MORRISON
Mayor, New Orleans, Louisiana

EDSON L. TENNYSON
Department of Public Property
Philadelphia, Pennsylvania

JOHN M. URIE
Research and Budget Officer
Phoenix, Arizona

advisers

WILLIAM E. WILLEY
State Highway Engineer
Arizona Highway Department
Phoenix, Arizona

JOHN W. BEATTY
Planning Director, Phoenix, Arizona

JOHN C. BOLLENS
Dept. of Political Science
University of California
Los Angeles, California

R. B. CAMPBELL
Assistant Traffic Engineer
Dept. of Highways
Toronto, Ontario

HOWARD GARDNER
Associate Director, League of
California Cities
Berkeley, California

NORMAN N. GILL
Director, Citizens' Governmental
Research Bureau, Inc.
Milwaukee, Wisconsin

DeWITT C. GREER
State Highway Engineer
Texas Highway Department
Austin, Texas

F. NORMAN HILL
President, Capitol Transit Co.
Little Rock, Arkansas

DAVID R. LEVIN
Chief, Land Studies Branch
Financial & Administrative
Research Division, U. S. Bureau of
Public Roads, Washington, D. C.

RALPH S. LEWIS
Chief, Financial & Administrative
Studies Section, U. S. Bureau of
Public Roads, Washington, D. C.

WILLIAM R. MacDOUGALL
General Manager, County Supervisors'
Association of California
Sacramento, California

PARK H. MARTIN
Executive Director, Allegheny
Conference on Community Development
Pittsburgh, Pennsylvania

JAMES MONTGOMERY
Transportation Economist
Financial & Administrative
Studies Section, U. S. Bureau of
Public Roads, Washington, D. C.

H. G. POPE
Executive Director, Public
Administration Service
Chicago, Illinois

Laws and Ordinances

STEPHEN CAREY, *Chairman*
Assistant Corporation Counsel
Detroit, Michigan

ALVIN DAHLEN
City Attorney, Jackson, Michigan

R. E. FRYER
General Counsel, Michigan
Municipal League
Ann Arbor, Michigan

FRANK E. HORAN
City Attorney
Albuquerque, New Mexico

ROBERT J. KELLY
Commissioner, Division of
Traffic Engineering & Parking
Cleveland, Ohio

WILLIAM McINTYRE
Assistant City Attorney
Nashville, Tennessee

W. VINCENT NASH
City Attorney, Saginaw, Michigan

HAROLD NEWCOMB
Corporation Counsel
Des Moines, Iowa

HOYT E. RAY
Deputy City Attorney
San Diego, California

ALAN H. STEINMETZ
Assistant City Attorney
Milwaukee, Wisconsin

THOMAS C. STRACHAN, JR.
General Attorney, Chicago
Transit Authority, Chicago, Illinois

NORMAN WILLIAMS, JR.
Director, City Planning Dept.
New York, New York

advisers

LOUIS R. MORONY
Director, Laws Division
Automotive Safety Foundation
Washington, D. C.

C. W. ENFIELD
General Counsel, U. S. Bureau of
Public Roads, Washington, D. C.

PHILIP P. GREEN
Assistant Director, Institute
of Government, University of
North Carolina, Chapel Hill
North Carolina

CHARLES M. HAAR
Department of Law, Harvard
University, Cambridge, Massachusetts

FRANK E. HORACK, JR.
Indiana University
School of Law, Bloomington, Indiana

DAVID R. LEVIN
Chief, Land Studies Branch
Financial & Administrative
Research Division, U. S. Bureau of
Public Roads, Washington, D. C.

JACK MERELMAN
Assistant General Counsel
National Institute of Municipal
Law Officers, Washington, D. C.

HAROLD S. SHEFELMAN
Weter, Roberts & Shefelman
Seattle, Washington

WILLIAM F. TEMPEST
Secretary, Section on Municipal
Law, American Bar Association
Chicago, Illinois

**Financial Records
and Reports**

R. F. AGARD, *Chairman*
Director of Finance
Kansas City, Missouri

DAVID V. ADDY
Auditor General
Detroit, Michigan

J. M. LOWERY
Auditor-Controller
Los Angeles County, California

THOMAS F. MAXWELL
City Manager, Norfolk, Virginia

P. J. MEINARDI
Comptroller, Chicago Transit
Authority, Chicago, Illinois

advisers

IRVING TENNER
CPA and Fiscal Consultant
Chicago, Illinois (deceased)

JOSEPH M. CUNNINGHAM
CPA and Systems Consultant
New York, New York

STUART A. MacCORKLE
Director, Institute of Public Affairs
University of Texas
Austin, Texas

LENNOX L. MOAK
Director, Bureau of Municipal
Research, Philadelphia
Pennsylvania

THOMAS R. TODD
Transportation Economist
Financial & Administrative
Research Study Division
U. S. Bureau of Public Roads
Washington, D. C.

Origin-Destination and Land Use

HONORABLE RICHARDSON DILWORTH, *Chairman*
Mayor, Philadelphia, Pennsylvania

EDMUND L. ENGEL
City Manager, Albuquerque, New Mexico

RICHARD GALLAGHER
Director of Public Works
San Diego, California

PHILIP E. GEISSAL
Chief Planning Engineer
City Plan Commission
Kansas City, Missouri

ALGER F. MALO
Director, Dept. of Streets and
Traffic, Detroit, Michigan

ROBERT C. STUART
Director, Metropolitan Planning
Commission, Atlanta, Georgia

advisers

J. DOUGLAS CARROLL, JR.
Director, Chicago Transportation
Survey, Chicago, Illinois

GLENN R. BROKKE
Highway Research Engineer
U. S. Bureau of Public Roads
Washington, D. C.

F. STUART CHAPIN, JR.
Dept. of City and Regional Planning
University of North Carolina
Chapel Hill, North Carolina

NATHAN CHERNIACK
Transportation Economist
Port of New York Authority
New York, New York

DONALD L. FOLEY
Associate Professor, Dept. of
City and Regional Planning
University of California
Berkeley, California

JOHN T. LYNCH
Chief, Highway Planning Survey
Section, Highway Transport
Research Branch, U. S. Bureau of
Public Roads, Washington, D. C.

ROBERT B. MITCHELL
Urban Traffic & Transportation
Board, Philadelphia, Pennsylvania

DANIEL O'FLAHERTY
Head, Traffic & Travel Studies
Section, U. S. Bureau of Public
Roads, Washington, D. C.

F. HOUSTON WYNN
Wilbur Smith & Associates
New Haven, Connecticut

**Measurement of
Existing Traffic Service**

LEO G. WILKIE, *Chairman*
Traffic Engineer
Cook County Dept. of Highways
Chicago, Illinois

ROGER T. CHANDLER
Traffic Engineer, City of
Providence, Rhode Island

HERMAN J. HOOSE
City Traffic Engineer
Charlotte, North Carolina

GEORGE W. HOWIE
Director of Public Utilities
and Traffic, Cincinnati, Ohio

HENRY W. OSBORNE
Traffic Engineer
Division of Safety
Buffalo, New York

VERNON THORPE
Public Works Director
Medford, Oregon

advisers

CARLTON C. ROBINSON
Traffic Engineer, Automotive
Safety Foundation
Washington, D. C.

DONALD S. BERRY
Professor of Civil Engineering
The Technological Institute
Northwestern University
Evanston, Illinois

ROBERT E. DUNN
Assistant Traffic Engineer
Washington Dept. of Highways
Olympia, Washington

H. A. MIKE FLANAKIN
Highway Engineer, American
Trucking Associations, Inc.
Washington, D. C.

S. T. HITCHCOCK
Chief, Highway Transport
Research Division, U. S. Bureau of
Public Roads, Washington, D. C.

BURTON W. MARSH
Director, Traffic Engineering
& Safety Department
American Automobile Association
Washington, D. C.

PAUL D. MUFFLEY
Planning Engineer, Pennsylvania
Dept. of Highways
Harrisburg, Pennsylvania

W. P. WALKER
Highway Design Engineer, Office
of Engineering, U. S. Bureau of
Public Roads, Washington, D. C.

**Inventory of the
Physical Street System**

WALTER H. TACKE, *Chairman*
Deputy Commissioner of Public
Works, Milwaukee, Wisconsin

ALFRED BERARDUCCI
Expressway Engineer, Dept. of
Public Works, Detroit, Michigan

MASON A. BUTCHER
Director of Public Works
Montgomery County
Rockville, Maryland

WARREN A. COOLIDGE
Director of Public Works
Nashville, Tennessee

KENNETH K. KING
Director of Public Works
Phoenix, Arizona

JOHN A. MORIN
City Engineer, Oakland, California

ALBERT G. WYLER
Director, Dept. of Streets
New Orleans, Louisiana
advisers

T. J. OWENS
Urban Highway Engineer
Automotive Safety Foundation
Washington, D. C.

F. B. FARRELL
Chief, Highway Cost Branch
U. S. Bureau of Public Roads
Washington, D. C.

R. W. GAMBLE
District Engineer, The Asphalt
Institute, Chicago, Illinois

GORDON GRONBERG
Head, Annual Cost Section
U. S. Bureau of Public Roads
Washington, D. C.

RALPH A. MOYER
Civil Engineering & Research
Dept., Institute of Transportation
& Traffic Engineering
University of California
Berkeley, California

GEORGE T. PAPAGEORGE
Field Representative, Urban
Renewal Administration
Atlanta, Georgia

JOHN G. SCHAUB
Special Assignment Engineer
State Highway Department
Lansing, Michigan

J. G. TRAPNELL
Highway Engineer, U. S. Bureau of
Public Roads, Washington, D. C.

**Measurement of
Existing Transit Service**

W. E. P. DUNCAN, *Chairman*
General Manager, Toronto Transit
Commission, Toronto, Ontario

VIII

KARL A. BEVINS
City Traffic Engineer
Atlanta, Georgia

LLOYD M. BRAFF
General Manager, Dept. of Traffic
Los Angeles, California

EDWARD DANA
General Manager
Metropolitan Transit Authority
Boston, Massachusetts

RALPH F. GROSS
Transit Engineer, City of
Chicago, Illinois

JOHN T. HANNA
Assistant Director of Public
Safety, Richmond, Virginia

LEO NOWICKI
General Manager, Detroit Street
Railways, Detroit, Michigan

advisers

WALTER S. RAINVILLE, JR.
Director of Research
American Transit Association
New York, New York

JOHN B. ECKER
Senior Engineer, W. C. Gilman & Co.
New York, New York

JAMES K. GIBSON
Principal Transportation Engineer
California Public Utilities Commission
San Francisco, California

WILLIAM R. McCONOCHIE
Chief Engineer, Traffic and
Transit Department
DeLeuw, Cather & Company
Chicago, Illinois

BURTON H. SEXTON
Traffic & Transportation
Consultant, Washington, D. C.

R. F. TYSON
Executive Vice President
Philadelphia Transportation Co.
Philadelphia, Pennsylvania

Standards for
Street Facilities and Services

EUGENE MAIER, *Chairman*
Director, Dept. of Traffic and
Transportation, Houston, Texas

CARL D. CANWELL
Commissioner of Public Safety
Spokane, Washington

RAYE C. EASTMAN
Planning Director
City of Ann Arbor, Michigan

OSCAR M. GUNDERSON
Planning Engineer, Board of
Wayne County Road Commissioners
Detroit, Michigan

EDWARD M. HALL
Transportation Research Director
City of San Diego, California

advisers

GORDON K. GRAVELLE
Deputy Commissioner, Dept. of
Traffic, New York, New York

WARREN T. ADAMS
Research Engineer, Highway
Transport Research Branch
U. S. Bureau of Public Roads
Washington, D. C.

WILLARD F. BABCOCK
Director of Highways, State Highway
& Public Works Commission
Raleigh, North Carolina

DAVID M. BALDWIN
Executive Secretary, Institute
of Traffic Engineers
Washington, D. C.

CHARLES B. BENNETT
Charles B. Bennett & Associates
Los Angeles, California

HARMER E. DAVIS
Director, Institute of Transportation
& Traffic Engineering
University of California
Richmond, California

HENRY K. EVANS
Manager, Western Division
Wilbur Smith & Associates
San Francisco, California

D. JACKSON FAUSTMAN
Consulting Traffic Engineer
Sacramento, California

JAMES O. GRANUM
Deputy Chief Engineer, Highways
Division, Automotive Safety
Foundation, Washington, D. C.

JOSEPH E. HAVENNER
Director, Engineering & Technical Service
Automobile Club of Southern California
Los Angeles, California

J. A. HEAD
Assistant Traffic Engineer
Oregon State Highway Dept.
Salem, Oregon

D. W. LOUTZENHEISER
Chief, Highway Design Division
U. S. Bureau of Public Roads
Washington, D. C.

A. WALTER NEUMANN
Director, Maintenance and Purchases
The Willet Company
Chicago, Illinois

O. K. NORMANN
Deputy Assistant Commissioner
for Research
U. S. Bureau of Public Roads
Washington, D. C.

THOMAS J. SEBURN
Associate Director, Bureau of
Highway Traffic, Yale University
New Haven, Connecticut

MAX S. WEHRLY
Executive Director, Urban Land
Institute, Washington, D. C.

**Standards for Transit
Services and Facilities**

DONALD C. HYDE, *Chairman*
General Manager, Cleveland
Transit System, Cleveland, Ohio

MICHAEL J. GITTENS
Traffic Engineer, Dept. of Public
Safety, Pittsburgh, Pennsylvania

LLOYD P. GRABER
General Manager, Seattle Transit
System, Seattle, Washington

VIRGIL E. GUNLOCK
Chairman, Chicago Transit
Authority, Chicago, Illinois

WARREN C. HYDE
Village Manager, Edina
Minneapolis, Minnesota

PAUL L. RISTROPH
Director, Dept. of Utilities
City of New Orleans, Louisiana

advisers

WALTER S. RAINVILLE, JR.
Director of Research, American
Transit Association, New York, New York

J. C. BAINE
President, St. Louis Public
Service Co., St. Louis, Missouri

J. L. HAUGH
President, San Diego Transit
System and Metropolitan Coach
Lines, San Diego, California

F. J. JOHNSON
President, Milwaukee & Suburban
Transport Co., Milwaukee, Wisconsin

ROSWELL F. THOMA
President, Niagara Frontier
Transit System, Inc.
Buffalo, New York

EDWARD G. WETZEL
Assistant Chief, Planning Division
Port of New York Authority
New York, New York

PREFACE

This handbook was prepared by the National Committee on Urban Transportation to help cities do a better job of transportation planning through systematic collection and analysis of basic facts.

The program outlined herein, created by many of the nation's foremost authorities, is adaptable to any community or metropolitan area. Techniques described are designed to guide the development of highway, transit, and terminal improvements in a manner which will (1) afford the public the best possible transportation service at the least possible cost; and (2) aid in accomplishing desirable goals of urban renewal and sound suburban growth.

This program has been endorsed by the Joint Committee of the American Municipal Association and the American Association of State Highway Officials, the American Transit Association, and numerous other national bodies.

It also has been endorsed by the Bureau of Public Roads, U. S. Department of Commerce, which has actively participated in its preparation. In general, the studies embraced in the program, if included in the statewide highway planning survey of any state wishing to cooperate in such studies, are eligible for financing assistance from federal-aid highway funds apportioned to the states, upon recommendation of the respective highway department and approval by the Bureau of Public Roads.

contents

better transportation for your city

INTRODUCTION

The daily movement of people and goods in urban areas has become one of the most complex and difficult problems facing public officials today. Only decisive action can stem the rising tide of traffic congestion, confusion, and accidents threatening the economic and social health of our communities. The Federal Aid Highway Act of 1956, with its unprecedented emphasis on urban needs, clearly recognized this fact.

Experience has demonstrated that piecemeal efforts are not the answer. A new approach is necessary if all the basic elements of the urban transportation problem are to be brought into focus and handled successfully. This calls for broad-gauge planning. It must be based on *facts* and aimed at balanced improvement of facilities and operations in all forms of local transport, in keeping with the broad objectives of community planning.

There are two main reasons why cities have failed to plan comprehensively to meet their transportation needs. One was lack of funds for extensive capital improvements. The other was lack of essential facts.

Fiscal limitations will now be eased, at least in part, as a result of the vastly increased federal aid for urban areas. As for the factual handicap, it can be permanently overcome by setting up the type of planning program spelled out in this Guide.

Data Vital for Decisions

For the administration of street and traffic affairs, as for any important decision-making responsibility, a complete set of facts and good evaluation techniques are indispensable.

Without a store of basic data, urban transportation problems cannot be accurately defined or measured. Without facts, it is hard to determine the potential solutions; it is even more difficult to select the most practical ones. Moreover, it is virtually impossible to present to legislative bodies and to the general public a clear picture of needs —or to create public understanding of the benefits that will accrue from improvements.

Just as the various forms of local transportation are interrelated and interdependent, so are there natural links and reciprocal values between different categories of transportation facts. Hence a well-rounded supply of information is a prime factor for successful integration of car, truck, and transit movements, in order to provide an optimum level of service. A solid factual foundation is the best approach to the sound development of long- and short-range plans for new facilities, and likewise to more efficient day-to-day operations. It is also vital for proper correlation of transportation planning and city planning.

New Era of Transportation

Lack of comprehensive data does not necessarily mean that improvements completed in recent years were not properly conceived or that obviously needed projects should be halted. But transportationwise, cities are now entering upon an era of great decisions. The challenges and opportunities ahead are enormous.

Urban highway modernization has lagged dangerously, while vehicular volumes continue to break all records. Traffic paralysis is spreading. Again, some rational balance will have to be found between the roles of public transit and private car transportation. Moreover, it will have to be recognized that the transportation problem cannot be divorced from problems of urban renewal and suburban development.

With municipal concern now deeply shared by state and federal authorities, the urban traffic plight is at long last receiving wide attention. Huge sums of money will be spent on highway improvements. It is important that these funds be used productively—in accordance with well-developed plans *based on fact*. Rule-of-thumb determinations or guesswork could be extremely costly in this big modernization program; and of course where fundamental data are not available, vital projects may be unduly delayed. Indeed, whether or not a city can take full advantage of the Federal Highway Program may well hinge on the factual documentation of transportation needs.

Some cities have conducted special factual studies now and then, with the resulting data directed to certain limited purposes. Very few communities, however, have ever set up an organized fact-finding program on a continuing basis, to provide a reservoir of working facts for *all* officials with responsibilities in urban transportation and development. Furthermore, simple and economical methods of processing the collected information, so as to serve a wide range of valuable uses, have been almost totally lacking.

How Facts Aid Officials

Adequate facts can help the municipal governing body in establishing transportation policy and desirable levels of service; the Chief Administrative Officer in determining how transportation improvements can be coordinated with other city activities; the City Planner in formulating long-range plans for development and capital improvements programing; the Traffic Engineer in operating the street system at maximum efficiency; the Director of Public Works and the City Engineer in designing street improvements and directing the street maintenance program; the Financial Officer in the preparation of the annual budget; and the City Attorney in drafting appropriate laws and ordinances.

Only on the basis of ample factual information can officials of transit companies, whether privately or municipally owned, hope to provide the optimum level of service consistent with sound economy.

Urban transportation data are also essential to state and federal legislators in determining allocations of funds, and to state and federal highway officials in cooperative construction projects in cities and metropolitan areas. It is significant that when legislation for the expanded highway program was being deliberated in Congress, factual data to demonstrate urban needs were conspicuously scarce whereas ample information was on hand about rural highway systems.

Lesson of State Planning Surveys

The reason for the disparity is that over two decades ago the U.S. Bureau of Public Roads and the State Highway Departments jointly set up the state planning surveys to maintain an up-to-date supply of facts about the systems under state jurisdiction. This program spelled out what data should be collected and how the collecting should be done. Thus there exists today a large backlog of useful information by means of which current and future needs may be accurately estimated.

In contrast, urban areas are largely without benefit of such accumulated information.

National Committee Formed

Recognizing this serious handicap, leading city officials from all over the nation banded together in 1954 to develop a practical system of fact collection and transportation planning adaptable to communities of all sizes. The organization which they formed to do this work is the National Committee on Urban Transportation, initially comprising representatives of the American Municipal Association, International City Managers' Association, American Society of Planning Officials, National Institute of Municipal Law Officers, American Public Works Association, and Municipal Finance Officers Association. Later the U.S. Bureau of Public Roads, the Canadian Federation of Mayors and Municipalities, and the National Association of County Officials also accepted membership. The American Association of State Highway Officials and American Transit Association are cooperating actively.

For its far-reaching task the National Committee has enlisted the aid of foremost authorities in transportation and related fields. A board of consultants was created to advise the Committee on the over-all program. Nine subcommittees were selected to deal with the various segments of the broad subject. These subcommittees are staffed by city and transit officials, as well as by technical specialists in particular fields. In all, more than 175 top experts are combining their talents and experience in this work.

Development of Guide

The Committee felt that the most valuable service it could perform for the cities would be to prepare a general guide or blueprint showing how a continuing transportation planning program can be set up in easy stages in every community. This has been accomplished with the publication of the present document, *Better Transportation for Your City*. To supplement this Guide, which is designed chiefly for administrative officials, a series of procedure manuals is being prepared for use by technicians in carrying out each stage of the program.

Establishment of an effective planning program involves many important factors—engineering, fiscal, legal, administrative, and others. All are vital, and all are fully treated in this Guide. What should appeal most to local governments is the fact that the complete system for developing technical information economically and on a uniform basis can be installed within the regular framework of city administration. Moreover, through various program modifications which have been worked out, even small communities can undertake it on a scale geared to their own needs and resources.

Main Benefits of Program

These, in brief, are some of the major benefits to be realized from the recommended program. It will help your city to:

1. Evaluate the soundness of existing transportation policies and practices.

2. Create a truly functional relation between transportation and city development.

3. Determine current transportation deficiencies and probable future needs, both facilities and operations, within the context of urban growth and foreseeable land-use changes.

4. Present legislative bodies and the public with fully documented reports on needs.

5. Prepare realistic plans to improve all forms of transportation service.

6. Establish priorities and permit continuous programing on a factual basis.

Key Features of Guide

In this Guide, recommended transportation standards have been formulated for the first time. It covers every phase of urban traffic facilitation.

The process of developing a workable, overall transportation plan is detailed step by step, along with techniques for setting up project priorities. Ways to chart an appropriate financing program are also described. Hence the Guide, together with the supplementary procedure manuals, can be of enormous help to all public officials concerned with the planning, construction, operation and maintenance of urban transportation systems.

Procedure Manuals Tested

To date, approximately 15 procedure manuals, showing how transportation data should be collected, analyzed, and evaluated, have been completed. (See list on insert page.) The techniques described fall generally into three categories: determination of basic transportation needs; evaluation of transport facilities; and appraisal of financial, legal, and administrative machinery.

Through the cooperation of several representative cities, certain of the procedures were first field tested under prevailing conditions and with existing departmental staffs. The procedures were then reviewed in light of results of the test applications and, where necessary, refined.

Significantly, these pilot operations revealed that many substantial indirect benefits—besides the major benefits aimed at—are generated when a comprehensive fact-finding program is installed. For example, here are some of the by-products in a single city:

The Director of Public Works succeeded in getting quick adoption and publication of a uniform map of the metropolitan area, though his efforts to do so in the past had been fruitless. The Traffic Engineer for the first time was afforded a complete inventory of the signs and signals in his area. This brought to light many signs he did not know about, and enabled him to eliminate needless duplications. The City Planner finally obtained the modern land-use survey he had wanted for a long time.

Intergovernmental Relations Improved

One benefit repeatedly noted in the pilot cities was the new spirit of teamwork and harmony which the project engendered. Since it brings key officials together in a continuous and mutually advantageous effort, it fosters closer intergovernmental relations. Moreover, in more than one instance, initiation of the program by a city has galvanized the interest of the entire area in their common transportation problems.

As more and more cities set up factual planning systems, the National Committee will draw on their experience and conclusions and, if warranted, incorporate desirable changes in the manuals. Procedures in a few phases, not yet fully explored, remain to be compiled in additional manuals. From time to time, new lists of manuals will be published. It is hoped that ultimately every worth-while technique of urban transportation planning will be placed at the disposal of cities everywhere.

ESTABLISHING A TRANSPORTATION PLANNING PROGRAM

This Guide is designed to help responsible officials develop a factual, orderly, and economical system of urban transportation planning—a system that will not only provide a more accurate perspective on needs and solutions, but will also result in improvement programs best calculated to win public acceptance.

A sound transportation planning program does not come about by chance. It cannot result from sporadic, single-purpose studies undertaken for the benefit of an individual agency. In dealing with urban transportation, no single municipal department, division, or unit can overcome all the problems on its own. No agency, whatever its functions in this complex field, can "go it alone." Both the fact-gathering and the improvement planning phases require close cooperation.

Importance of Teamwork

Since the eventual improvement plan, if it is to be comprehensive and well balanced, must be shaped on the basis of data developed from many sources by numerous agencies, the importance of teamwork cannot be overemphasized. Moreover, proper machinery must be set up to insure *continuity* of intergovernmental coordination.

It is one of the special values of the Guide approach that all officials with transportation responsibilities in city government are brought into active partnership from the beginning. In the main, their roles in the various phases of the program can be performed within the compass of their regular duties—without disruption of normal routines and with relatively modest additional cost.

Facts Repay Investment

Once the studies required for the reservoir of technical data have been completed, most of them can be kept up to date inexpensively by occasional limited samplings. The numerous advantages accruing to the city from having ample information to deal factually with perplexing street and traffic problems will repay the initial investment over and over again.

However, merely charting a sound, factually supported program will not alone produce the requisite improvements. The plan for priority and long-range improvements must be correlated with a long-range financing plan which will provide intelligent guidance for the annual budget. Only in this way can proposed physical and operational betterments be translated into reality—into a higher level of transportation service to benefit the whole community.

Six Basic Stages

Experience indicates that a successful transportation planning program can be developed best in six orderly steps or stages, which may be briefly listed as follows:

STAGE I —Organizing for the Job

STAGE II —Getting the Transportation Facts

STAGE III—Defining the Problem

STAGE IV—Developing the Transportation Plan and Financial Program

STAGE V —Adopting the Preferred Plan and Financial Program

STAGE VI—Carrying Out the Plan

These stages (highlighted in the functional chart, Figure 1) have been adapted as the basic framework of this Guide. They provide a simple and logical sequence for officials to follow in carrying out the general procedure recommended.

Figure 1   **ESTABLISHING A TRANSPORTATION PLANNING PROGRAM**

LEGISLATIVE BODY

TECHNICAL COORDINATING COMMITTEE
MUNICIPAL REPRESENTATIVES
    Municipal Departments and
    Agencies
    Transit Management

REPRESENTATIVES OF COOPERATING AGENCIES
    Cooperating Cities
    County, State, and Federal
    Officials
    Representatives of Special
    Agencies or Authorities

CHIEF ADMINISTRATOR

TRANSPORTATION PLANNING
PROGRAM DIRECTOR

CITIZENS' ADVISORY COMMITTEE

Citizen Groups
and Organizations

Business, Professional,
and Labor

Stage I
ORGANIZING

Stage II
GETTING THE FACTS

| Street Use | Physical Street System | Existing Traffic Service | Existing Transit Service | Origin — Destination and Land Use | Financial Records |

Individual Study Reports

Stage III
DEFINING THE PROBLEM

Technical Coordinating Committee

Report of Analysis of
the Transportation Facts
1. Existing Conditions
2. Future Land Use and Travel Patterns
3. Standards
4. Deficiencies

Citizens' Advisory Committee

Stage IV
PREPARING THE PLAN

Technical Coordinating Committee

Report on
Transportation Plan and
Financial Program
1. Alternative Proposals
2. Financial Programs
3. Evaluation of Proposals

Citizens' Advisory Committee

Stage V
OBTAINING PLAN APPROVAL

Technical Coordinating Committee

Public Information

Legislative Action

Citizens' Advisory Committee

Stage VI
PUTTING THE PLAN TO WORK

Technical Coordinating Committee

CARRYING OUT THE PLAN
1. Establishing Priorities
2. Coordinating the Work
3. Keeping the Plan up to Date

Citizens' Advisory Committee

Legislative Body

Annual Budget

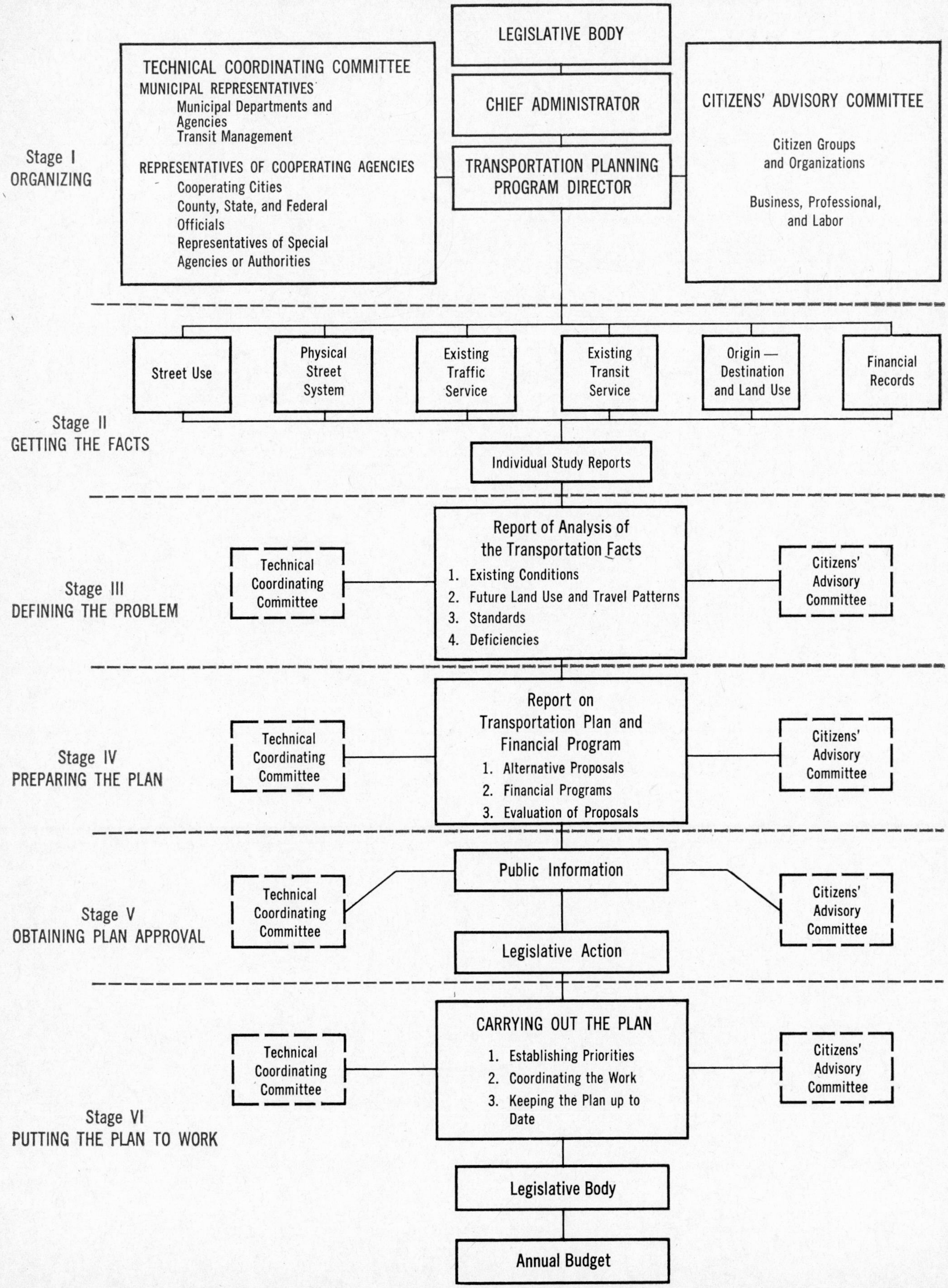

STAGE 1: ORGANIZING FOR THE JOB

The crucial test of the transportation planning program comes right at the start. It must be effectively organized or it simply won't produce. For it is at this initial stage that the scope of the program is decided, the respective roles of the cooperating agencies are fixed and their responsibilities defined. The fact that few cities have understood the importance of proper organization explains why the full potential of transportation planning has never yet been brought to bear on the urban traffic muddle.

In essence, the setting-up stage of the planning program involves (1) obtaining legislative approval, (2) establishing technical coordination, and (3) developing public support.

LEGISLATIVE APPROVAL

It is of the utmost importance when initiating this program that approval be obtained from the City Council or other legislative body. Before the Council is approached, however, the Chief Administrator, in consultation with department heads, probably will want to work up some kind of prospectus for the proposal.

The department officials should have the opportunity to familiarize themselves with the basic phases and requirements set forth in the Guide. With that background, they can provide at least a rough appraisal of what the over-all job will involve. Preliminary discussions with county, state, and federal officials can determine to what extent other levels of government can contribute assistance—personnel and/or funds—to help defray the costs. It might be well also to confer with officials of adjacent communities to determine to what extent they might be interested in undertaking similar programs. From these various sources, an estimate of costs and manpower can be developed to lay before the Council, along with the purposes and advantages of the transportation program.

Council approval should have the force of a legislative mandate—calling for the individual participation of all pertinent agencies of municipal government, as well as their joint cooperation; directing that progress reports be supplied to the legislators; and making sure that the necessary budget is provided to carry out the program.

APPOINTMENT OF DIRECTOR

Once the Council has given the green light, the Chief Administrator can proceed with the organization job. In larger cities, it undoubtedly will call for appointment of a Program Director to supervise the program and keep it moving. The Director might be a staff member of the Planning Commission, the Traffic Engineering Department, or the Department of Public Works. After appointment, he may continue his status with his agency, or he may be given special status making him responsible to the Chief Administrator.

In the smaller communities, the Program Director logically might be the City Planner, the Director of Public Works, or the Traffic Engineer. It may be feasible for him to supervise the over-all transportation program while continuing his regular activities.

Whatever the size of the city, however, arrangements should be such as to allow the Director to spend sufficient time on essential administrative matters, neglect of which could impair the program.

As his first task, the Director will work with the Chief Administrator in establishing two cooperating groups which are indispensable to the program—a *Technical Coordinating Committee* and a *Citizens' Advisory Committee*.

TECHNICAL COORDINATING COMMITTEE

Actually serving as the operating staff for the entire program, the Technical Coordinating Committee should comprise key officials of municipal departments and other agencies directly concerned with local transportation, including privately owned transit and parking authorities. The unit, however, should not be so large as to be unwieldy.

Individually, these officials will head up the fact-finding projects to be undertaken by their respective agencies. As a committee, they will articulate both the study and the planning phases. They will serve as a clearinghouse for assembly and evaluation of all pertinent data, in line with over-all city objectives. They will exchange ideas on possible solutions. Finally, they will constitute the planning team which, on the basis of factually demonstrated needs, can evolve a sound transportation improvement plan keyed to healthy community development.

In the case of big cities, particularly those of focal importance in a metropolitan area, representatives of other levels of government, with mutual interests in the area traffic problem, should be invited to serve on the Committee.

Generally speaking, each city and local government in a metropolitan area should form its own Technical Coordinating Committee, which also could be represented in a similar organization set up for areawide planning where appropriate. Though each city will scale its study program to meet its own requirements, the information it compiles will help to round out the total area picture.

Cities in metropolitan areas will find it advantageous to tie in their own programs with a joint transportation planning effort for the area as a whole. Each urban place adds to—and in turn is influenced by—the traffic complex generated by the area. Hence the transportation problem is in reality a composite of the problems of all the communities in the grouping. This fact emphasizes the need, now being increasingly recognized, of coordinated thinking and planning.

As a rule, the largest or parent city is in the best position to initiate areawide planning. Smaller cities commonly look to the central city for leadership in such cooperative undertakings. Moreover, the central city usually has technical staff available to lend guidance and assistance to its smaller neighbors.

Coordination on City Level

It has been stated that the Technical Coordinating Committee for the city's transportation program should be made up of departmental officials and should have transit representation. Though their titles will vary in different municipalities, typical members might include the Director of Public Works or City Engineer, the Traffic Engineer, the City Planner, the Transit Manager, the City Attorney, and the Finance Officer.

In small communities it may not be feasible to assign more than two or three officials to the transportation program, and perhaps only on a part-time basis. Nevertheless, even with its limitations, such a unit can perform a significant service by conducting useful studies. For even the little city today is plagued with traffic and parking troubles, and seldom does it have the facts needed to determine the most effective remedies.

All of the municipal officials represented on the Coordinating Committee have vital roles, particularly in the study phases which will produce the factual foundation on which the over-all transportation program will be based.

The City Engineer (or Director of Public Works), for instance, will be responsible for carrying out the street inventory cataloguing the physical features and condition of the existing street system—such as street widths, rights of way, pavement types, age, and condition, location of curbs and gutters, and storm sewers.

The Traffic Engineer will, among other things, make an evaluation of existing traffic service with reference to such aspects as volume, capacity, travel times, accident rates, parking conditions, and the general adequacy of present control measures and devices.

The City Planner will develop a land-use survey, and will participate in certain of the studies which will prove useful in coordinating the transportation plan with the general city plan.

The Transit Manager will make analyses of existing transit service, including routes and their coverage, passenger route patterns, frequency of service, travel times, and passenger riding habits.

These officials will combine their efforts in determination of street use, upon which is predicated the proper classification of the facilities. These same people will be involved to various degrees in appraising deficiencies in present transportation service. As a team they will ultimately create an over-all improvement plan geared to community development; and along with the Chief Administrator or his assistant, they will advise with the Finance Officer in shaping a fiscal program to implement the plan.

The primary task of the Finance Officer will be to establish accounting procedures whereby he can segregate all costs relating to construction, operation, and maintenance of traffic facilities, on the basis of systems and segments of systems. In this way he will be able to report completely on sources of revenue, how and where spent, and debts incurred.

The City Attorney, too, has an important role on the Coordinating Committee. He is the legal adviser to all the participating departments. He therefore must understand the responsibilities and objectives of his colleagues on the Committee. He must sit in with them at the various study and planning stages, helping to find solutions where matters of law are involved. The elements which he should consider in working with the Committee are briefly outlined in the section of this Guide on "Modernizing Laws and Ordinances"; they are treated in detail in a special manual. Adequate legal tools will be essential. Many cities today are hampered by horse-and-buggy laws in their efforts to step up modernization of their street plants.

Finally, when an over-all transportation improvement plan is approved by the the City Council, the City Attorney will be responsible for drafting the necessary legislation to carry it out.

Metropolitan Coordination

In the case of metropolitan areas consisting of several large communities with technical staffs, each normally would set up its own Coordinating Committee, with membership including the same types of officials as just described.

In metropolitan areas consisting of only one large city and several small satellite communities or urbanized county territory, it probably will be more feasible merely to expand the central city's Coordinating Committee to include representatives from the other jurisdictions.

Other levels of government and numerous special agencies have a stake in metropolitan transportation, and as a rule will welcome the chance to participate in the work of the Committee. Federal agencies would include the Bureau of Public Roads (which would be represented through its Division office), and possibly branches of the Armed Forces, where local transportation problems impinge on military or naval installations. The State Highway Department would be represented by one of its engineers; a county by the Highway or Traffic Engineer or the Planning Director.

Indeed, state and federal participation will be a salient factor in the success of the metropolitan transportation program. Virtually all the Interstate System mileage in urban areas and many of the urban extensions of other trunk lines of the Federal-Aid Systems will be improved to serve metropolitan traffic. This improvement will necessitate close cooperation in the planning, financing, and construction of the facilities.

It is well to keep in mind, too, that Federal-Aid "planning funds" are available through the State Highway Departments and can be used to defray a considerable part of the cost of certain of the recommended engineering studies. (This subject is discussed in more detail in the Stage II section of this Guide.)

Typical of the special agencies which doubtless would want to be represented on the Metropolitan Area Coordinating Committee are areawide Park and Recreation Boards, Transit Agencies, Port Authorities, and Toll Bridge Authorities.

Recently in a number of metropolitan areas, Regional Planning Commissions—newly formed because of the availability of Federal Housing and Home Finance Agency funds—have set up coordinating groups similar to the type described.

As has been indicated, the Coordinating Committee will function as the basic "operating force" for the entire program.

After organization of the Coordinating Committee, whether local or metropolitan, the members and Program Director should decide on the general scope of the studies to be undertaken. The role of each member (and of the department or agency which he represents) should be clearly defined. All should fully understand how their individual roles fit into the over-all program. Then a definite work schedule should be mutually agreed upon and the study phases set in motion. Findings of each study should be embodied in appropriate reports, which will form the basis of the later fact-evaluation and planning stages.

CITIZENS' ADVISORY COMMITTEE

The second key group in establishing a transportation program is the Citizens' Advisory Committee, which serves as a spearhead for public support. Whether the improvement plan which the Coordinating Committee ultimately will recommend to the city will stand or fall will depend largely upon the degree of understanding and acceptance that has been generated among the citizen body. An essential step, therefore, is the formation of a strong support group drawn from various civic, service, safety, traffic, and parking

A well-informed Citizens' Advisory Committee is the spearhead of public support for the ultimate program of transportation improvement. The group should be frequently briefed by the technical experts during the fact-finding and planning stages.

organizations and including leaders of business, industry, labor, farm, and professional groups.

The Citizens' Advisory Committee is usually appointed by the Mayor. The chairman of such a group in each community may be designated to serve on an areawide council or committee for a metropolitan program.

The citizens' group can render effective support only if it is properly indoctrinated in the objectives and benefits of the transportation program—and is enabled to take an active part. Not only should the members be kept informed of developments through periodic briefing sessions, but wherever possible they should be given specific jobs to do, so that they can feel they are making a useful contribution.

To create an Advisory Committee and then let it remain dormant during the technical fact-finding and planning stages may lose its support later at the critical time when the recommended improvement plan is placed before the public.

As a matter of fact, such citizen groups often can provide valuable assistance to the Coordinating Committee even in the study phases. They could be particularly helpful in smaller cities where the number of working personnel is limited.

Support Group Activities

For example, with proper supervision, a participating organization like the Junior Chamber of Commerce might enlist its members to aid in volume studies. Service clubs and youth groups might help in cordon counts. The local trucking association might keep records of time runs and assist in spotting congestion and making checks of loading zones. The auto club might make a parking check. Other voluntary groups could be employed in other ways.

Women's clubs could perform a valuable service by conducting a campaign to explain the Origin-Destination Study and to prepare people throughout the community for the interviews necessary to carry it out. The truckers should be asked to cooperate to the fullest extent in carrying out truck interview studies. In this case, the trucking representative on the public support group could inform all the local carriers that they will be approached for information on their truck movements during a particular day.

In carrying out the parking study, the downtown merchants can help to create the right atmosphere by publicizing its purpose and importance and encouraging participation of citizens in the necessary interviews.

Colleges and universities, now becoming increasingly aware of the services they can render the community in the field of transportation, are another valuable source of aid. Their contribution to the municipal transportation program can take the form of technical counsel, summer student help, loans of equipment, and so on.

And of course the Citizens' Advisory Committee will be a potent force in the development of an effective public information program. It should enlist every possible medium—radio, television, the newspapers, magazines, speakers' bureaus, and so on—to get the story over to the people. The public should be fully apprised of the economic and social implications of the program, the extent of present transportation deficiencies, the obstacles facing their officials, the need for action. In short, the biggest job of the Advisory Committee will be to mobilize an informed public opinion.

With a properly organized Technical Committee, backed up by aggressive public support, any city can blueprint—and carry out—a rational program of transportation improvements in keeping both with its requirements and with its available resources.

The growing seriousness of urban traffic problems, with their mounting penalties in lives and dollars, dictates that every community should act quickly. Some may feel they are not in a position to undertake a full-scale study program because of lack of personnel or other reasons. They should remember, however, that the recommended program is of a *continuing* nature. Therefore, cities unable to join at the time initial projects are undertaken in their metropolitan area can start at a later date and still contribute to the long-range success of the total program.

STAGE II: GETTING THE TRANSPORTATION FACTS

Having organized the transportation planning program in Stage I, the next step is to set up the work program to provide an adequate factual base of information. This stage includes the following studies:

1. Street Use

2. Origin-Destination and Land Use

3. Existing Level of Traffic Service

4. Existing Level of Transit Service

5. Inventory of the Physical Street System

6. Financial Records and Reports

Time spent in properly planning the work program will be saved many times over in the course of carrying out the required investigations. The Technical Coordinating Committee should fully understand the objectives of each phase of the study program and give careful thought to the role each member will fill and the responsibilities to be assumed by the different agencies of local government concerned. Such planning applies both to the initial studies and to the subsequent follow-up to maintain the information up to date.

In the interests of efficiency, these studies should be conducted concurrently because the data to be developed are interdependent and must be used in combination to produce good usable facts. Each study is a well-defined part of the total informational picture to be developed.

Not all studies must begin simultaneously, but it is preferable that all studies, or a particular series of studies, be completed at approximately the same time. This procedure is recommended so that the entire base of information to be developed for a community may be considered and reviewed as a complete entity. Since some studies will require more time, manpower, and expenditure than others, work should be planned so that personnel and funds are apportioned to best advantage.

The investigations embraced in the fact-finding stage will be the responsibility of those operating departments of the city normally concerned with transportation matters.

Federal and State Aid

Conducting this series of important studies for the first time doubtless will entail some additional expenditures. Fortunately the local government need bear only a portion of the cost. Under the various Federal-Aid Highway Acts, notably the 1956 Act, up to 1.5 per cent of the federal funds apportioned to the states are available for engineering and planning purposes.

For example, if a state is apportioned $20 million by the Federal Government for highway purposes in a particular year, 1.5 per cent of that total, or $300,000 in federal funds, would be available in that state for "engineering and economic investigations." Customarily the total amount of the 1.5 per cent funds, or such portion thereof as may be used for the purpose, is complemented by state funds, or by state and local funds.

Federal funds allocated to states for engineering and economic investigations are intended for statewide use and may be applied in both urban and rural areas. Use of these funds in particular political subdivisions is at the option of the respective State Highway Departments, upon approval of specific studies by the U.S. Bureau of Public Roads.

Before a city attempts to undertake these studies, it is recommended that the Program Director contact the State Highway Engineer and present the proposed study program. Upon review, the State Highway Engineer will be in a position to advise local officials as to relevant policy followed by the State Highway Department and the funds available for the proposed studies. He may also make suggestions and through his staff offer such technical assistance as the department can extend. It is esssential that a working agreement with regard to the responsibilities of each party and the procedures and policies to be followed be established before the study program is started, in order to minimize the possibility of misunderstandings at a later date.

Generally, the various phases of the planning program outlined in this Guide are qualified for federal funds apportioned to State Highway Departments for engineering and planning purposes. Such funds, however, may not be used for studies dealing with transit operations, local administration, local laws and ordinances, or investigations of a similar nature.

In addition to the so-called "1.5 per cent funds," there are federal funds which are available for general planning purposes from the Federal Housing and Home Finance Agency. This aid is authorized under Section 701 of the Federal Housing Act of 1954 as amended and may be used for transportation planning as part of the over-all planning program. Such funds are available to official State Planning Agencies for planning assistance to cities of less than 25,000 and to Regional and Metropolitan Planning Agencies approved by the Housing and Home Finance Agency.

Section 702 of this act also provides for advances of funds to any nonfederal public agency for preliminary and detailed planning for all types of public works, including transportation facilities such as streets and highways, bridges, viaducts, traffic control, and related work for which other federal funds are not currently available. These advances are provided in the form of interest-free loans which are repayable when construction is undertaken.

Early in Stage II the Technical Coordinating Committee should get together with the Citizens' Advisory Committee and explain the fact-gathering operation—going into the types of facts that will be obtained and the reasons for getting them. The public support group should be briefed in detail on those parts of the operation where its direct assistance may be required.

STREET USE

The objective of this study is to identify all streets according to their present use. This should be the first investigation undertaken by the community, since the findings are needed for other phases of the fact-gathering program, particularly the determination of the existing level of traffic service, the preparation of an inventory of the physical street system, and the financial records study.

Determination of street use on a street-by-street basis would be a very time-consuming and costly process. For the purposes of this program, an adequate working concept of street use can be developed by drawing on the knowledge of Coordinating Committee members familiar with the characteristics of traffic patterns in the city.

In designating street use, it is recommended that all streets be assigned to one of these four categories: (1) Expressways, (2) Major Arterial Streets, (3) Collectors, and (4) Local Streets. The traffic functions of each category are explained in a procedure manual, which should be referred to in conducting this phase of the study.

Before launching a Street Use Study, it is often helpful to consider a more or less theoretical street pattern, such as the one shown in Figure 2, or to review the pattern of a newly developed area in the community where it is easy to distinguish between the purposes of the various streets.

In exploring either a hypothetical or an actual situation, the Committee should visualize the nature of the traffic that would be on the various kinds of streets. For example, what are the characteristics of the traffic on a typical day? Is the movement local in character—i.e., does the majority of the travel begin and terminate in the immediate vicinity? If so, it probably should be designated a Local Street.

When the Committee has established a common base for distinguishing differences in the traffic characteristics of various streets, the whole street plant can then be brought under analysis. This process is not too time consuming.

Street Use Map

It is suggested that the street use determinations be indicated on a map with appropriate color symbols for the various classes. This map should be kept up to date as streets and traffic patterns are changed. Street use often goes in cycles. For example, a street in a new area may start out as a purely local residential facility. When extended, it may act more or less as a collector. Eventually, when tied in with an expressway, it may serve as a major arterial. On the other hand, a new freeway, by reducing through traffic on a nearby arterial, may change its function to a local business street.

In a continuing transportation program, such evolutions should be noted and recorded periodically. Each change in the street use map should be agreed to by all agencies involved, so that the

Figure 2　　DIAGRAMMATIC LAYOUT FOR A RESIDENTIAL AREA

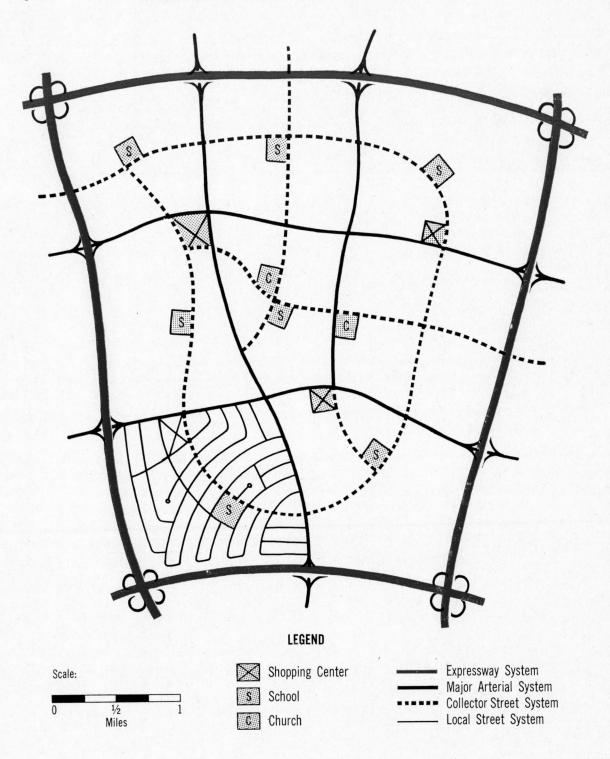

LEGEND

Scale:

0　　½　　1
Miles

⊠ Shopping Center
Ⓢ School
Ⓒ Church

━━━ Expressway System
━━━ Major Arterial System
▪▪▪▪ Collector Street System
──── Local Street System

13

information collected by them severally will be related to a common classification system.

In developing a street use map, however, it should be understood that it is not the ultimate classification plan of the streets, nor should it be construed as the master street plan. The map merely indicates how the streets are being used and the traffic functions they are performing today.

ORIGIN-DESTINATION AND LAND USE

If the community has not completed an Origin-Destination Study within the past 10 years, it is recommended that one be undertaken as soon as possible.

There are other important values—for example, in developing land use plans. Data on the traffic generating characteristics of varied land uses, and on the transportation linkage these uses require, are essential if sound interrelations are to be embodied in the general plan.

Conducting Origin-Destination Surveys

Preliminary to setting up an O-D Survey, a city or metropolitan area should consult with the State Highway Department, since most state highway agencies have had considerable experience in the O-D study field and can be extremely helpful. Furthermore, the state agency may be in a

The Origin-Destination Study reveals the underlying factors of urban movement. Because modern traffic knows no boundaries, the cooperation of several government levels is often required in this type of survey.

The purpose of an Origin-Destination Survey is to develop information on the number of trips into, within, and through the city, the mode of travel used, and the time of day the trips are made.

These data, compiled through interviews and questionnaires, are the source material for later appraisal of transportation deficiencies—transit and street needs and parking and loading requirements. The same facts will be useful in locating and designing freeways, expressways, major streets, bridges, and rapid transit facilities, as well as in arranging bus routes and schedules.

Such information, too, is valuable to legislative bodies, particularly in formulating over-all planning policies. The data can be used as a guide in establishing the proper relation between urban transit and automobile services and facilities.

position to contribute special federal and state funds which are available for such studies.

Since the O-D Survey is the most time consuming and complicated in the whole fact-finding operation, it is strongly recommended that a special staff be created, and that the technical personnel assigned to it be relieved of all other responsibilities. Staff may be drawn from two or three of the cooperating municipal departments, but if they cannot be spared by the departments it may be necessary to employ outside personnel.

In preparing the O-D questionnaire and deciding on the technical aspects of the survey, the staff should consult closely with the Coordinating Committee, so that the many-sided potential of this work is achieved. Through slight adjustments in the study, for example, it may be possible to develop a great deal of special information required by individual Coordinating Committee members. As an illustration, the interviews could produce facts on shopper riding habits which the Transit Manager could use without making a special investigation. Similarly, the O-D Survey can develop data which can simplify the work involved in other studies.

Methods Keyed to City Size

Various kinds of studies have been devised to obtain origin and destination data, each designed to evaluate a certain type of traffic problem. Which method a community should employ depends largely upon the local traffic situation. In small communities where the transportation problem is relatively simple, a broad-scale investigation is not necessary. Any technique which can define general travel patterns should be adequate. In large metropolitan areas a much more comprehensive type of survey is called for. Accordingly the following methods (described later in this section) are recommended for various-sized cities with different types of traffic problems.

Urban Areas Under 5,000 Population

A simple External Cordon Survey will suffice in urban areas under 5,000 population, since in most cases outside traffic exerts the major influence on the traffic patterns within such an area. Furthermore, traffic movements not recorded through this technique are not stable enough to have any significant impact on long-range plans.

Urban Areas Between 5,000 and 75,000 Population

An External Cordon Survey should give adequate information in cities between 5,000 and 75,000 population in which the predominant traffic flow is on through routes, few complications are imposed on the over-all street pattern, and transit is not much of a factor.

An External-Internal Cordon Survey should be conducted in cities where most of the traffic is oriented toward the downtown district, or where the movement is mostly through traffic, and no major deficiencies in the street system exist outside the downtown area.

An External Cordon-Parking Survey is recommended in cities where congestion and parking problems are concentrated in the central business district and where but few traffic problems exist outside this area.

An External Cordon-Home Interview Survey is recommended where major traffic problems are found throughout a city, or where there are a sufficient number of transit riders to present significant routing problems.

Urban Areas Over 75,000 Population

In places of over 75,000 population, it is recommended that an External Cordon-Home Interview Survey be conducted. The size of the samples used should be scaled to particular needs of the community and to the degree of accuracy required.

Description of O-D Methods

The following description highlights the main features of the methods used to obtain O-D data. Full particulars on how these techniques should be carried out will be found in the procedure manuals on the subject.

External Cordon Survey

The External Cordon Survey is a roadside interview type of study in which drivers are stopped and asked certain questions about their trip—its origin and destination and its purpose. The interviews are conducted at stations located where major roads cross the "external cordon"—an imaginary line drawn around the urban area under study.

At these stations the number and type of all vehicles passing the station are recorded. Only a portion of the drivers need be interviewed, though the interview period is only one or two days and the cost per interview is small. It is important, however, to obtain a sufficiently large sample to be representative. Size of sample will depend, of course, upon the traffic volume of the roads under consideration.

External-Internal Cordon Survey

The external cordon part of the External-Internal Cordon Survey is conducted, as previously described, by interviewing a sample of drivers. In addition, a parking study is made in the downtown area. Parkers at the curb are interviewed to obtain information as to the origin, time, and purpose of the trip, as well as their destination after the car is stored.

The information developed from the External Cordon Survey, along with the origin-destination data obtained from parkers, will give a fairly complete picture of traffic patterns in smaller cities where the bulk of the traffic is destined for the central business district.

External Cordon-Home Interview Survey

The technique for the External Cordon-Home Interview Survey was developed by the U.S. Bureau of Public Roads. A series of interviews are conducted to cover a selected cross section of dwelling units throughout the urban area. Besides obtaining the origin and destination of trips made by the residents, information is compiled on the time, purpose, and mode of travel used for these trips during weekdays (Figure 3). Data on car ownership and population also are derived from these studies.

In conjunction with these home interviews, a proportion of the truck and taxicab owners in the area should be interviewed to obtain information on the amount of use of such vehicles.

These interviews should not be limited to a single day. In fact, it is recommended that they be spread out over a year's time to afford a better picture of the year-round traffic pattern.

Along with these interviews, a portion of the drivers passing the external cordon line should be interviewed to record data on out-of-town vehicles. The information obtained from the external cordon, combined with the data obtained from the dwelling unit, truck, and taxicab interviews, will give a comprehensive picture of all weekday travel habits within the urban area.

Technical Procedures

Before conducting any of the studies described, it is important to determine how the information will be collected, evaluated, and analyzed. These factors should be considered in designing the questionnaire form and in determining the method for conducting the interviews. The possibility of recording information on a grid coordinate basis should be considered.

Smaller cities may find it desirable to tranfer the information obtained from the interviews to "Keysort" cards. In larger cities it is recommended that the information be transferred to punched cards to permit mechanical tabulation of the data. The use of punched cards will greatly assist in the expansion of the data and in speeding up detailed summaries and analyses.

Land Use

Data on land use are essential for the development of an over-all land use plan, which log-ically should precede or parallel a transportation study. Furthermore, to project traffic patterns with reasonable accuracy, it is necessary to determine the relation between various land uses and traffic generation.

In other words, anticipated land use provides a basis for estimating future travel patterns.

In most cases, land use information is collected as a normal activity of the local planning agency or commission. Therefore, before undertaking an Origin-Destination Study, it is advisable that the planning agency or agencies be consulted to see what information is already available, what additional facts will be required, and how such a study can be most efficiently conducted.

Frequency of Studies

To repeat, any city which has not completed an Origin-Destination Study within the past decade should conduct one now. Dynamic changes that occur in the size of population, in economic and social conditions, land uses, motor and vehicle registrations in the space of ten years have a decided influence on traffic patterns. These induced changes or evolutions in community traffic patterns can be determined only through periodic study.

In addition, all municipalities should make an effort to keep their origin-destination data fully current during the intervals between studies by means of a perpetual inventory of land use and traffic movement.

Cities planning home interview origin-destination surveys or repeat studies should conduct them preferably during the same year as the census of population is taken. This will help to facilitate sampling procedures and will also minimize the difficulties of bringing census information up to date.

To this end, the possibility of using census enumerators in carrying out these studies should be explored at the local level.

Periodic review of origin-destination data will be helpful in fields other than transportation. It will show the City Planner and the businessman what functional changes have been occurring in land uses in the urban area and will also indicate patterns of growth.

Cost of Study

Since these studies are fairly involved and will take considerable manpower, they are rather expensive; in fact. the cost will usually be more

Figure 3

DWELLING UNIT INTERVIEW FORM

INTERNAL TRIP REPORT

SHEET .... OF ....

CARD [2]   TRACT [ ][ ]   BLOCK [ ][ ]   SAMPLE No. [ ][ ]   SUBZONE [ ]   DAY OF TRAVEL [ ]

1	2	3	4	5	6	7	8	9	10	11
OCCUPATION AND INDUSTRY	PERSON NO.	TRIP NO.	SEX AND RACE	Where Did This Trip Begin?	Where Did This Trip End?	Mode of Travel	Time of— Starting / Arrival	Purpose of Trip (From / To)	No. in Car Including Driver	Kind of Parking

Column 4 — SEX AND RACE: 1, 2, 3, 4, 5, 6

Column 5 / 6: City

Column 7 — Mode of Travel:
1 Auto Driver
2 Auto Pass.
3 Street-car-Bus
4 Taxi Pass.
5 Truck Pass.

Column 8 — Time of—: Starting A.M. / P.M.; Arrival A.M. / P.M.

Column 9 — Purpose of Trip (From / To):
1 — Work — 1
2 — Business — 3
3 — Med.-Den. — 3
4 — School —
5 — Social, Rec. — 5
6 — Ch. Travel Mode — 6
7 — Eat meal — 7
8 — Shopping —
9 — Serve pass. — 9
0 — Home. — 0

Column 11 — Kind of Parking:
1 Street free
2 Street meter
3 Lot free
4 Lot paid
5 Garage free
6 Garage paid
7 Service or repairs
8 Res. property
9 Cruised
0 Not parked

Revised: October 1954

17

than the total of all the other transportation studies conducted in Stage II. The range of costs for obtaining the data and properly recording them on punched cards is roughly as follows:

	COST
External Cordon Survey	
Cities up to 75,000	$ 2,000 –$ 10,000
External-Internal Cordon Survey	
Cities up to 75,000	10,000 – 15,000
External Cordon-Parking Survey	
Cities up to 75,000	20,000 – 30,000
External Cordon-Home Interview Survey	
Cities from 50,000 to 150,000	30,000 – 85,000
Cities from 150,000 to 300,000	68,000 – 135,000
Cities from 300,000 to 500,000	85,000 – 150,000
Cities from 500,000 to 1,000,000	112,000 – 225,000
Cities with 1 million and over	180,000 – 1,000,000

Actual cost will depend upon sample size selected, personnel required, need for office space, and various other overhead items.

A note of caution with particular reference to the O-D Study should be sounded here. Information obtained through haphazard interviews will not only result in inadequate data, but will greatly hamper later analysis. Utmost care, therefore, must be taken to get the right facts and record them correctly.

EXISTING TRAFFIC SERVICE

Few elements of transportation planning are more important than sound appraisal of existing traffic services. Listed below is a series of recommended studies designed to provide basic indexes and facts whereby valid measurement can be made of the existing level of traffic service in any city. By keeping the resulting data current, it will be possible to keep tabs on any changes in the level of service.

Traffic Volume
Travel Time
Street Capacity
Accidents
Parking
Control Devices

All of these investigations come within the province of the Traffic Engineer or other individual carrying out traffic engineering activities. In larger cities, it probably would be well for the Traffic Engineer to delegate the study responsibilities to a person who can devote full time to following through on the whole series. Such delegation would insure better coordination for what are, in fact, related studies.

Some of the indicated studies are already being conducted in many places, and it is doubtful that any large number of cities will find it necessary to inaugurate the entire list as new work. Even where it is necessary to do the whole group, they need not be conducted simultaneously. The interrelation between them, evident from the description below, will in itself suggest a logical order for undertaking them.

It will be noted later that, for each type of study, a specific schedule of frequency is suggested. There is good reason for this recommendation. The information to be assembled will have its greatest value for comparative purposes, and this value will not be fully realized until sufficient data have been collected to allow effective comparison. For example, the volume of traffic crossing some arbitrary line dividing the city is an interesting but not too significant statistic when considered alone. If, however, this volume has been measured for a number of years and shows a consistent annual growth, valuable information has been obtained.

Thus, each of the separate studies in this phase is meant to supply certain pieces of information of maximum value when related to the other studies of the program. The Traffic Volume Study, for instance, provides the quantitative information needed for the completion of most of the other studies recommended.

Individual cities may wish to expand parts of the suggested study schedule in order to develop the details and precision necessary for their particular operational needs. Such expansion may be highly desirable if it does not endanger, by its magnitude, the total scope or continuous nature of the program. It is strongly recommended that the minimum program, as described, be completed in all of its aspects before any one phase is enlarged.

Traffic Volume

Statistics on vehicular volume afford a quantitative yardstick of the transportation system. To obtain complete accuracy in measuring average daily traffic, it would be necessary to count vehicles continuously for a year on every stretch of road within the city. Needless to say, the cost of such a count would be prohibitively high. On the other hand, it is feasible to use a plan based on sampling which will provide volume figures of the necessary degree of accuracy—and at a minimum cost to the city.

Traffic volumes vary from hour to hour, day to day, and month to month, but it is the average daily traffic throughout the year and the traffic at certain peak hours which the counting program seeks to determine. Control counts at a few carefully selected locations make it possible to adjust short-time sampling counts that are made on other streets. Thus it becomes relatively simple to estimate the average daily and peak-hour traffic flows on individual sections of the major system.

Another important step in the traffic tallying phase is the cordon line count. The cordon line should be established to circumscribe the central business district and the area and streets generally used for parking by persons making trips downtown. This count is made in order to determine the mode of travel, the hourly variation in arrivals downtown, and the changes taking place in these items with the passage of time. The count is also a basic tool in the preparation of the Parking Study.

A third operation is the screen line count, which is intended to provide data on annual trends of vehicular trips within the city. Location of the screen line should take advantage of natural barriers (like a river, for instance) so as to entail a minimum number of counting stations.

It should be kept in mind that the continuous nature of this program requires that counts be scheduled far in advance and that the schedule be diligently followed.

Travel Time

Many studies have demonstrated that the automobile driver measures the desirability of a route on the basis of the total travel time it takes to reach his destination. In evaluating the service performed by the street system, the time measure must be given great weight. Time is, in fact, the only measure of the quality of highway service that is uniformly understood and free from serious differences in interpretation.

Time lost in traversing an area is an index of congestion and may be translated into monetary terms more readily than any other yardstick devised to date. Travel time also is valuable in computing the amount of use that a new facility will receive, as well as in estimating the benefits to be derived from such a facility.

Measurement of travel time on the major street system will reveal the comparative level of service on different segments and on the entire system at different periods. In many cases, such measurement also will serve to locate points of greatest delay and will suggest possible remedial action. Many traffic control techniques, for instance, are devoted primarily to expediting traffic movement, and their value may be appraised in

terms of travel time.

The travel time study is performed by a driver and observer traveling over the major street system. The driver operates the vehicle at the "average" speed, while the observer records the time as designated control sections are reached. These raw data are used to determine the factors of speed and time.

It is recommended that the evening peak-hour travel time in the direction of predominant traffic flow be determined for the entire major street system.

These investigations should be repeated at least every two years.

Street Capacity

The vehicular capacities of major street intersections are an index of the capacity of the street system as a whole.

Capacity of an intersection is dependent upon its geometric characteristics, such as surface width of intersecting streets, and also upon such variables as composition of traffic, percentage of vehicles making turns, and the kind of traffic and parking controls in operation. Though the effect of and relations between such variables are imperfectly known, it has been possible to develop a reasonably accurate method of measuring capacity at specific times.

The procedure manual for street capacity outlines this measuring technique, as formulated by the Highway Research Board in its *Highway Capacity Manual*.

Since certain of the variable factors change during the course of a day, capacity is usually computed on the basis of peak-hour conditions. Normally this is the evening rush hour, though at some locations the peak traffic may occur at other times.

In determining the capacity of an intersection, volume counts at the peak hour are taken by a recorder, who also lists the types of vehicles and the turning movements made. Likewise noted are the percentage of green signal time, parking restrictions at the intersection, and the total width between curbs of the crossing leg of the intersection under study. From these data it is fairly simple, with the special tables and charts available for the purpose, to make the necessary computations.

The Capacity Study provides pertinent information on the adequacy of the present street system. With capacity determined, and with predictions of traffic volumes that can be made for specific future years on the basis of traffic volume and O-D data, an estimate can be made as to when the traffic saturation point will be reached on any street.

It is recommended that a capacity analysis be made at all intersections of two major streets and at other critical locations. These intersections as a rule will constitute about 5 per cent of the total intersections in a city.

Accident Study

The service expected from a city street system is safe, convenient, and efficient movement of people and goods. Studies previously discussed measure only the efficiency, and to some extent the convenience, of the street system. For a complete appraisal of the system's performance, information on the degree of safety afforded to the users also is necessary.

In many localities, traffic accident information is collected and analyzed more effectively than data on any of the other aspects of street service. One reason is that accident facts are of value to a number of other agencies besides the engineering units. The state motor vehicle authority, city police, courts, safety and education groups, and other organizations have an interest in accident statistics.

The principal engineering uses of accident information are as a measure of the adequacy of segments of the street system and as an indication of the effectiveness of control measures—or the need for them, where none exist. A high accident rate at a certain location, or at certain times at specific locations, usually spells some sort of physical or operational deficiency.

The Accident Study can be made by using the city's existing accident records system if it is adequate. For communities where accident records are either incomplete or unobtainable, detailed instructions for setting up an accident rec-

First step in any realistic approach to the parking problem is an inventory of available facilities in critical areas of the city. Besides supply and location, the time pattern and duration of use must be determined.

ords system are provided in the procedure manual on the subject. Accident rates are computed for the major street system and to depict citywide accident trends.

There are three main elements in this phase —studies of high accident locations and accident rates and a uniform summary of accident data. These steps are outlined in the procedure manual, together with instructions on how to establish an accident location file and fill out the Abbreviated Accident Information Form.

Parking

Terminal facilities for automobile and truck parking (or loading) are as much a part of the transportation system as the streets and highways that carry moving traffic. Complete transportation service implies getting the motorist from origin of trip to final destination. It includes the temporary storage of the vehicle if the trip must be completed on foot. Time lost in parking and walking from the parking place to destination often offsets any increase in service brought about by improvements in the street system itself.

Shortages of parking and other terminal facilities as a rule are most critical in the central business district, and the recommended studies concern that area principally. Inadequate parking and loading facilities elsewhere, however, may in some cases pose an equally important problem to the city, and should not be ignored. The recommended study, generally speaking, is applicable to any district.

A Parking Study will help to provide answers to such knotty questions as whether curb parking spaces are being properly used; whether time limits should be adjusted; and whether more police enforcement should be applied. It will also be valuable to the legislative body in appraising off-street parking policy—for instance, whether new buildings should be required to provide offstreet parking under the zoning ordinance.

One aspect of the Parking Study explores supply, and is in essence an inventory of locations and number of existing parking and loading spaces, the regulations and restrictions applying to that supply, and the areas potentially available for terminal facilities.

The second, or use, phase of the study determines the degree of utilization of the supply, the time pattern and duration of use, and the violations of existing regulations. This information is obtained both through field investigations and through analysis of parking meter receipts. The findings provide a basis for estimating the extent of parking deficiencies (if they exist) and how well supply is keeping up with demand in a district as a whole. The data also serve as a general guide to the locations where supply is short, but a more detailed survey will be required to determine exact deficiencies at specific points.

Control Devices

In a real sense, traffic control devices are intended chiefly to compensate for certain inherent limitations in street and highway systems. A theoretically perfect system would require none, with the possible exception of directional signs. The more outmoded a facility is (and the street networks of most of our cities are anything but modern), the greater the need for control devices, as a general rule. Thus, major arterials must be protected by stop signs; critical capacity problems must be met by parking prohibitions; important intersections must be controlled by traffic signals and often by prohibitions against turning.

The recommended inventory of these devices will, therefore, indicate broadly how well the physical limitations of the street system are being compensated for—in the interests of transportation efficiency.

Traffic control devices also are the evidences of government administration with which the average citizen is probably most familiar. From their intelligibility, appearance, and effectiveness, he often may judge the caliber of municipal government. This reason alone would dictate the proper use and maintenance of control devices. But even more important, these devices exert a legal control over the citizen's everyday activity and affect his safety, time, and money.

Clearly, then, a sound traffic control system is an absolute "must" for any community. Such a system should embrace proper warrants and standards, as well as a perpetual inventory of use to facilitate inspection and maintenance.

A well-rounded study of traffic control measures should comprise these three ingredients:

a. An inventory of major control devices
b. An inventory of major parking regulations
c. An inventory of transit routes, including loading zones and physical street features related to transit operations

Another significant aspect which deserves attention is uniformity of control devices. Over the years there has evolved a tremendous diversity of signs, signals, and markings. This welter of differing mechanical devices is a source of confusion, inconvenience, and, in many cases, of actual danger to motorists and pedestrians. Recognizing the growing seriousness of the problem, transportation authorities called for the creation of a set of standards for use by cities and states. These are now embodied in what is known as the *Manual on Uniform Traffic Control Devices,* which is kept current by periodic revision.

When a community makes its inventory of control devices, therefore, this manual should be used for checking uniformity with the nationally accepted standards.

Cost of Traffic Services Study

As has been already brought out, some cities are conducting studies similar to those recommended in this program and have accumulated some of the basic data. Hence it is difficult to generalize about the probable cost of carrying out the Traffic Services Study phase of the program.

It is possible, however, to arrive at a relatively accurate cost figure (in terms of man-hours) if a particular community is starting from scratch. Approximately 10 to 20 man-hours per 1,000 population per year will be required to conduct the six projects dealt with in this section. Included is the time needed to collect the data in the field and to tabulate them.

This figure assumes that the work schedule will be maintained on a uniform basis over a period of five years. If the program is telescoped into a couple of years, then the costs for the five-year program naturally will have to be allocated over the shorter period. In other words, the annual cost will depend upon how the study is scheduled.

Existing Transit Service

Measurement of the level of existing transit service has been actively pursued by the more progressive transit companies for many years, normally with their own staffs on a continuing basis. The aim of such study has been to improve transit routing and operations generally. Seldom, however, are the findings employed for a further purpose of great importance—as a vital segment of the comprehensive data needed to bring the total urban transportation picture into focus.

And yet, unless cities begin using a coordinated approach, their growing traffic problems will never get solved. The only real hope is in developing a balanced system of transportation that utilizes each form of transportation, both private and public, to best advantage. Such development demands an integrated program of fact collection

and analysis. It requires that transit information be compiled so as to be usable in conjunction with the other kinds of traffic data already discussed.

In the case of a publicly owned transit system, it would seem superfluous to impress upon city officials that the transit problem is inseparable from the total traffic problem—and that municipal responsibility demands that transit issues be dealt with within the factual context of urban transport as a whole.

As for private transit companies, the incentive for a coordinated factual approach, though perhaps not so obvious, is hardly less compelling. It is essential that the service, problems, and requirements of the private company be put into clear perspective if it hopes to make a strong case for such municipal aids as may be needed for a healthy transit operation. Moreover, the cooperative study program herein recommended offers an excellent opportunity for better relations between privately owned transit and the city it serves.

Therefore, the studies in this section have been designed not only to provide transit management with a sound technique for evaluating present service—with the ultimate goal of maximum efficiency and economy—but also to pave the way for integrating transit with urban planning and the over-all transportation policy of the community.

The study components include:

> Routes and Coverage
> Transit Route Inventory
> Passenger Load Data
> Service Frequency and Regularity
> Transit Running Time
> Transit Speeds and Delays
> General Operating Data
> Passenger Riding Habits

Where a single transit company operates within a metropolitan area, it should assume responsibility for carrying out the series of required studies. If there is more than one company or agency, and the general study program is on an areawide basis, the work should be a joint enterprise of the transit group. All transit data should then be coordinated and analyzed, and combined summaries should be prepared. This work should be done by the transit experts in concert with the representatives of other interested agencies serving on the Coordinating Committee.

Comparison of the summarized transit data with the standards described in Stage III will reveal the extent of any current deficiencies.

Since the studies are periodic in character, a

In any study of transportation efficiency, it is important to know how well other sections of the city are linked with the downtown area through public transit.

suggested schedule of frequency is included. Data thus accumulated over a term of years will become increasingly valuable to the transit company, and should lead to better-planned and more productive operations.

Routes and Coverage

Measurement of transit route coverage in an urban area not only serves to appraise the adequacy of the transit service being offered the community, but also helps to point up remediable deficiencies. Such tests of adequacy may be applied in terms of the present distribution of population, and also of potential future distribution.

Fundamentally, there are three steps in this type of measurement:

1. Determining whether all populated areas of sufficient density to justify transit service are now being served in accordance with accepted standards of routing. This process involves use of a background map of the area to plot existing transit routes and reasonable walking distances therefrom.

2. Ascertaining whether the transit routes are sufficiently related to public desires and movements to make transit riding reasonably direct and convenient. The "desire lines" pattern will have been previously established from the communitywide O-D Study discussed in an earlier section.

23

3. Establishing a "coverage ratio," using supplementary data on population distribution developed in related studies. As described in the procedure manual, the coverage ratio may be recalculated from time to time, as a means of revealing to what extent transit service is keeping pace with the needs of community growth and development.

Cost of this work should be nominal, since it requires only the preparation of maps and the obtaining of transit travel information from O-D material—if both the O-D and the population data have been compiled as part of the comprehensive fact-finding program of the community. Figure 4 illustrates a typical transit route map.

Route coverage should be brought up to date and the coverage ratio recalculated every five years. Comparison of transit routings with the origin-destination "transit travel desires," as well as with general travel desires, should be made at 10-year intervals to coincide with the suggested O-D Survey program.

Transit Route Inventory

As already indicated, a survey of the physical characteristics of each transit route is usually made as part of the Existing Traffic Service Study. The information obtained in this survey should be made available to the transit company, which should assist in developing a system for keeping the inventory up to date as a cooperative project.

The transit route inventory ultimately can produce substantial benefits to the riding public, since it provides a basis for improvement in the physical characteristics of transit routes and hence improvement in the quality of service rendered.

Passenger Load Data

Adequate and properly handled passenger-load data are the starting point for the transit schedule-maker in the routine adjustment of schedules to provide service in accordance with the number of people who wish to ride the system at various periods of the day, on various days of the week, and during different seasons of the year.

It is the general practice of the transit industry, therefore, to check the lines of the system regularly in order to determine the volume of passenger traffic which must be carried. Transit passenger loads are observed and recorded at predetermined points where the heaviest loads occur. (This point is known to most transit concerns.) Such checks, usually referred to as "checks at the maximum load point," are carried out by manually counting the numbers of people who pass the maximum load point of the route per given time period.

Passenger-load information, when properly summarized in accordance with the details set forth in the procedure manual, can be compared with the capacities and time schedules of transit vehicle movements past the maximum load point to provide the basis for adjustment of schedules to a level of adequate service. Furthermore, the data on arrival time obtained from these studies can be used to determine service frequency and regularity.

Where cordon counts of vehicles and passengers are to be conducted by city traffic officials, simultaneous passenger-load counts should be made by the transit company to record the corresponding movements of passengers and transit vehicles, as previously suggested. A satisfactory checking schedule might include three weekdays—Tuesday, Wednesday, and Thursday—in a normal-season month such as May or October.

Service Frequency and Regularity

Measurement of transit service frequency and regularity is of value in maintaining a high level of performance. It provides:

1. A basis for appraising the adequacy of present transit service by comparing present service frequencies with recommended frequency standards.

2. A basis for similarly appraising service regularity. A by-product can be the detection and removal of underlying causes of service delays and interruptions, whether "internally" or "externally" caused.

When these data are correlated with findings from the communitywide studies of traffic travel time and studies of transit running time, speed, and delay, they pave the way for action by city traffic and police officials to correct congestion-inducing conditions which impair transit service. Results of this line of investigation can be improvement in regularity of service, fewer costly delays, better distribution of passenger loads, and reduction of service interruptions.

Measurement of frequency of service, of the regularity of service (uniformity of headways), and the degree of adherence to the schedules is directly related to passenger-load studies. Because the arrival time of vehicles at maximum load points is recorded in passenger load checks, the Load Study automatically determines the actual frequency of service, and its regularity, at that point.

Figure 4

AREAS SERVED BY TRANSIT — METROPOLITAN ATLANTA

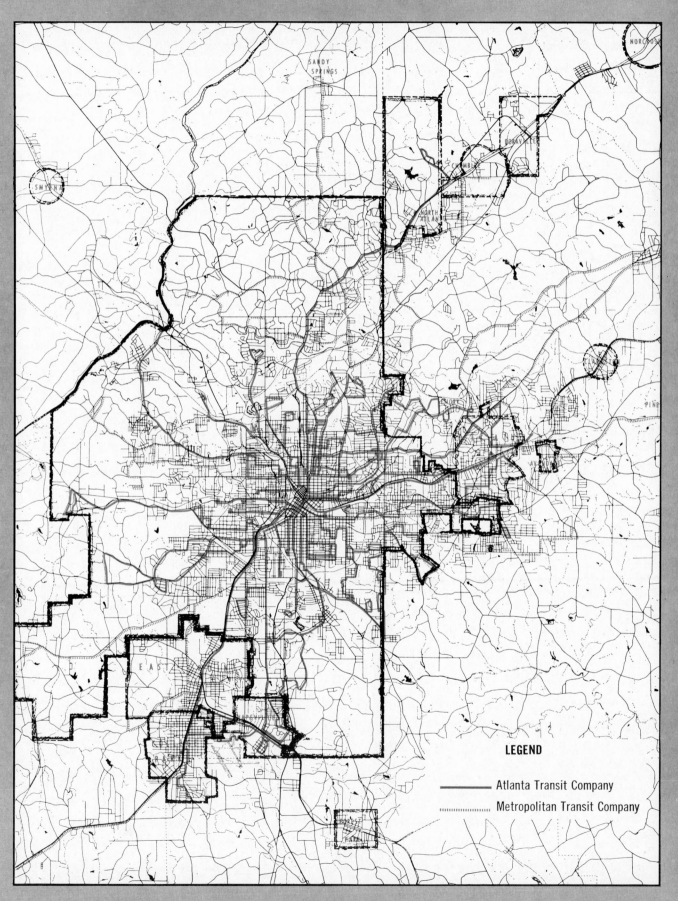

LEGEND

—————— Atlanta Transit Company

·············· Metropolitan Transit Company

Measurement of service frequency and regularity at other than maximum load points is usually a separate operation, to be applied especially on heavier routes.

Transit Running Time Studies

Transit running time, synonymous with passenger "travel time," is a measure of the convenience which the transit service provides the public and of the efficiency of the schedule and its relative cost of operation.

Studies of running time require that a checker be placed on the bus to record travel time and speeds.

Schedule speed is the primary factor in the efficient use of transit rolling stock. Where passenger traffic is handled over a sustained period, it is the schedule speed which determines whether vehicles will make their runs in time to begin another productive trip in the prevailing direction of passenger movement, or whether other vehicles must be "pulled out" to meet the need, with attendant fixed charges and high-ratio operating costs.

For the sake both of public convenience and of economy of operation it is important, therefore, that a transit schedule-maker have at his disposal adequate data upon which to base an estimate of required running time. The closer this speed corresponds to the speed of general traffic movement the better, assuming of course that general traffic moves freely, without congestion and delay.

Transit companies, in seeking minimum travel time for their passengers, give attention to the variations which take place in running time during different seasons of the year, on different days of the week, and at different hours in a single day. Every effort is made to take account of the variations in conditions to minimize interference and delays. If situations subject to correction are found, such as parking interference, unusual signal delays, or similar traffic impediments, it may be necessary to restudy certain portions of the route through the use of more detailed Transit Speed and Delay Survey techniques.

Transit Speed and Delay Studies

The purpose of measuring transit speed and delay is to identify controllable causes of delay to traffic movement, and to point the way toward overcoming them. Improvements that tend to benefit the speed performance and time convenience of the transit system usually also improve the flow of general traffic.

Speed and Delay Surveys are made by transit companies whenever the results of service regularity and running time investigations indicate the need for more detailed analysis of certain parts of a transit route. The portions most frequently studied will be the high-volume density streets, such as those in the central business district or in congested outlying commercial centers.

General Operating Data

Measurement of the level of urban transit service from year to year, as an index of progress, should include an evaluation of certain general operating characteristics. This information, as indicated in Table 1, should be compiled on an annual basis for the individual metropolitan area under study. Such data are normally available and need only to be tabulated.

The suggested yardsticks must *not* be used for comparison of one city with another. Because of the differences in geographical, topographical, and distance factors, in distribution of population, in distribution of automobile ownership, and in levels of income and economic activity, comparisons between different cities in terms of these suggested yardsticks may result in misleading and unfair conclusions. The adequacy of existing levels of transit service in any community can best be determined by measuring them and comparing the findings with the standards given in Stage III.

The six yardsticks recommended for year-to-year comparisons of transit service levels in a city are:

1. *Quantity of service*—vehicle miles per capita
2. *Quality of service*—vehicle miles per 100 revenue passengers
3. *Efficiency of service*—terminal-to-terminal time per vehicle mile
4. *Use of service*—revenue passengers per capita
5. *Route coverage*—route miles per 1,000 persons (based only on those persons who reside in areas of sufficient population density to support transit services)
6. *Time Convenience*—operating system speed (m.p.h.)

An additional factor which might be used—and it is really a measure of the "competitive background" against which transit operations are conducted in the typical city today—is the number of registered automobiles per capita.

Table 1
SUGGESTED SUMMARY TABLE
Operating Statistics by Years

BASIC DATA (For total metropolitan area)	1955	1956	1957	1958	1959	1960	1961
Area served (sq. mi.)							
Population served							
Revenue passengers							
Registered automobiles							
Transit route miles							
Transit vehicle miles (revenue)							
Transit vehicle hours (revenue)							
Terminal to terminal time							
YARDSTICKS							
Vehicle miles per capita							
Vehicle miles per 100 revenue passengers							
Terminal-to-terminal time per vehicle mile							
Revenue passengers per capita							
Route miles per 1,000 passengers							
Operating system speed							

Passenger Riding Habits

Information obtained in the Origin-Destination Studies, if reported in terms of transit rides per zone, can be very helpful in determining relationships between automobile ownership, population density, and transit rides per capita. These facts may prove of value in making estimates of potential revenue in areas where the transit company is investigating the economic feasibility of future service extensions (see Stage III), or in avoiding wasteful duplications of service.

Origin-destination data may also be useful in determining certain aspects of transit travel habits —for instance, the average lengths of transit passenger rides. This information may aid the transit company in cost-of-service studies, zone fare research, and collateral studies.

PHYSICAL STREET SYSTEM

Facts about the physical features of specific streets are available from various sources in many cities, but rarely is the information compiled so as to permit the kind of comprehensive analysis that is needed for transportation planning purposes.

27

Every business executive recognizes that, to run a successful enterprise, he must keep fully informed as to his plant, his equipment, and his capital assets. For the same reason, city administrators should be armed with all the facts on municipal facilities for moving people and goods.

Such information can be used for many purposes, such as determining street needs, short-term and long-range planning, maintenance budgeting, and even answering complaints.

One of the collateral benefits is a better knowledge of the life expectancy of various pavement types under various traffic conditions. For example, the inventory might reveal that, over the

Comprehensive facts about the physical street system are essential for both short-term and long-range planning. Data on curb-to-curb widths, pavement types, age and condition, and so forth, should be properly recorded for ready evaluation in developing these plans.

next 10 years, 75 miles of street pavement could be expected to require replacement and 150 miles resurfacing. A suitable program could then be initiated to do part of this work each year.

Here are some typical questions for which a well-maintained inventory will help to supply answers:

How many structures does the city actually have to maintain? What is their condition, and when will they need replacement for structural reasons?

Does the city have enough right of way for necessary street widenings?

What type of pavement has proved best for downtown? For arterial streets? For residential streets? To provide this type of data, the inventory covers a span of years.

Items in Inventory

In carrying out the study, it is recommended that an inventory sheet be prepared to record data about different street segments. Information on curb-to-curb widths, right-of-way widths, pavement types, age and condition, riding quality, condition of sidewalks, curb, and gutters, storm drains, and type of illumination should be obtained from existing records or from field checks and placed on the recommended form.

In addition, facts should be gathered about railroad crossings at grade and structures like bridges, viaducts, and tunnels. General data on such facilities are collected on a special form prepared solely for that purpose. Much of the material may have to be obtained by field surveys.

The length of street sections decided upon should reflect local needs. The longest sections that can be effectively used are those having substantially the same curb-to-curb width, pavement type, and traffic volume. When any of these items change, a new sheet should be started. It may also be desirable to start a new sheet when the administrative classification changes.

Some communities will prefer to establish their inventory on a block-plus-intersection basis, regardless of change in these items. While this procedure entails more sheets, it has the distinct advantage of permitting the recording of future changes with minimum effort.

Recording the Data

Many cities, particularly large ones, will find it advantageous to transfer inventory data to punched cards so that certain data can be extracted and summarized in a short time. In some instances, it may be worth while to transfer certain information to a map or a series of maps, presenting the data by color code or some form of symbol.

Methods for maintaining inventory data will vary according to the size of the community and the use to be made of the information. Simply filing the work sheets is the easiest but least serviceable method. The most productive use of the information calls for transfer of the data to punched cards according to a coding plan. In this way any portion of the recorded data can be segregated and tabulated. A punched card system makes it possible to have at one's fingertips such specific facts as the number of total miles of certain categories of facilities; the square yardage of various surface types; the sections with unsatisfactory riding qualities; the streets expected to require replacement in "x" years; miles of state highways; and similar information.

The inventory can be made when there is a slack in the work load. It does not have to be scheduled for any particular time and, if systematized, much of the job can be done by subengineer grades. However, a review of the status of present street conditions and life expectancy of the facilities will call for a person with considerable background in construction and maintenance. If relatively long sections are used, it seldom will require more than two man-days per mile to develop and record the necessary data for the entire street system. Use of personnel familiar with the street system can save much time.

FINANCIAL RECORDS

Summary records of revenues and expenditures are prepared routinely by all local governments. Seldom, however, are they presented in a manner helpful to legislative bodies in developing over-all transportation policy or to administrative officials in reviewing current practices and establishing the work program. Consequently, the object of this phase of Stage II is to produce fiscal information which, collected and kept up to date on a uniform and continuing basis, will have maximum value for transportation purposes.

Specifically, such information will help the legislative body to crystallize policy on:

1. Allocation of funds related to (a) various street systems, (b) maintenance, operation, and new construction, and (c) various means of transportation

2. Sources of transportation revenues

For the administrator, such data will be useful in:

1. Estimating costs of new construction, street maintenance, and transportation operations

2. Preparing the annual budget

3. Preparing a capital improvement program

4. Evaluating administrative practices, including the determination of what work should be done by force account or by contract, and how personnel and equipment can be used most effectively

Financial records must be kept in a form that will be helpful to legislative bodies in developing transportation policy and to administrative officials in reviewing existing practices and programs.

The responsibility for carrying out this study should be assigned to the Chief Fiscal Officer, who is represented on the Technical Coordinating Committee. Before undertaking this study, it will be necessary for the Chief Fiscal Officer to meet with all affected departments and agencies to decide the specific procedure to be followed by each to produce the desired information at the least possible cost. These decisions should be reached in cooperation with the respective departments and should include the actual costs to be recorded, the cost details required, the forms to be used, and the reporting procedures and schedule to be followed. The procedure manual on Financial Records and Reports outlines these steps in detail.

Besides the Chief Fiscal Officer, the department heads and agencies normally involved will include the Director of Public Works or City Engineer, the Traffic Engineer, the Police Chief, Transit Management, and special authorities having transportation functions such as bridge, tunnel, or parking responsibilities.

After agreement on the program has been reached, responsibility for maintaining the necessary accounts should be fixed. In many instances the accounts will be maintained by the Chief Fiscal Officer; in others, detail accounts supporting the central control accounts may be put in charge of the operating departments.

The Fiscal Officer will have the duty of assembling these data and preparing the necessary summaries. It should be stressed that the collected information will be factual only to the degree that the basic data supplied from all sources are correctly provided. Many accounting and cost systems fail to portray the true fiscal picture because operating departments do not cooperate in providing precise data.

Information To Be Developed

The procedure manual suggests that the fiscal information should cover both privately and publicly operated facilities. Provision is also made for reporting, where available, data concerning urban street expenditures made directly by the state, by a county, or other agency. Transportation items included would be streets, bridges, tunnels, storm sewers, traffic control, parking, and publicly and privately owned and operated transportation lines such as streetcar, bus, and subway systems.

Summary report forms have been developed to facilitate and guide the collection of the basic information required. Sample forms, as well as the procedures to be followed in compiling the data, are presented in the procedure manual.

These summary report forms cover six areas:

1. Revenues, nonrevenue receipts, and expenditures pertaining to general facilities

2. Revenues, nonrevenue receipts, and expenditures pertaining to public service enterprises

3. Investment in fixed assets

4. Indebtedness

5. Statistical data summarizing transportation revenues, expenditures, and related information over a period of several fiscal years

6. Cost accounting—developing a cost accounting system for transportation purposes

This information, gathered on an annual basis, will reveal the different types of transportation expenditures, their purpose, and total transportation costs. It will permit legislative and administrative officials to evaluate existing fiscal policy more objectively, and thereby help to speed up decisions on demonstrated transportation needs.

Accounting Systems

Information on municipal finances is usually obtainable in most cities. Nevertheless, in order to develop adequate statistics on transportation expenditures and operational costs, it may be necessary to make adjustments in the accounting system in use. It is recognized that not all communities have a standard accounting system, and while some may have all or most of the necessary cost information available, others will not. In cities where a different system of accounting is used, or where the system is specified by charter or state law, a parallel or auxiliary accounting system may have to be created to provide the information recommended.

Fund Accounting

Municipalities establish funds to insure compliance with legal and administrative provisions. A fund has been defined by the National Committee on Governmental Accounting as a "sum of money or other resources segregated for the purpose of carrying on specific activities or attaining certain objectives in accordance with special regulations, restrictions, or limitations and constituting an independent fiscal and accounting entity."

The procedure manual describes the various funds that as a rule should be established in a community. The transportation data contained in different fund records must be combined to arrive at the total revenues and nonrevenue receipts available for financing transportation facilities or the total amount expended for such facilities and their operation. Methods of allocating funds are also described in the manual.

In analyzing the financial data it is necessary to know under which of the three bases of accounting they have been prepared, namely, cash basis, accrual basis, or modified cash basis.

It is recommended that as far as practicable the accrual basis of accounting be followed, because it reflects revenues and expenditures more accurately than either of the other two bases. Accordingly, the procedure manual is based on the assumption that the accrual method will be followed. However, the data can be compiled equally well under the cash basis or the modified cash basis. It is important at all times to indicate the basis of accounting under which the data have been compiled.

Cost Accounting

The procedure manual presents a system of cost accounting for transportation purposes. Cost accounting is a method which provides for the assembling and recording of all of the elements of cost incurred to accomplish a purpose, carry out an activity or operation, or complete a unit of work or a specific job. Accounting for transportation costs is basic to the development of adequate financial information that will be useful in appraising the existing program in light of future needs.

The aim of the accounting procedure is to establish the main elements of actual cost related to the planning, construction, maintenance, and operation of a transportation system. To achieve this objective, detailed records must be kept for all activities pertaining to transportation. Included should be the amount of labor, equipment, materials, and overhead expenses. This information, when properly analyzed, makes it possible to evaluate administrative practices and work programs. It helps to determine, for example, whether machinery is being used with maximum efficiency; when such equipment should be replaced; where the cost of street and highway maintenance warrants reconstruction; and what might be the most effective use of available personnel. A cost accounting system will also develop unit costs for labor, materials, and equipment which are necessary in estimating the costs of future programs and operations.

The actual cost of gathering the information recommended will depend to a large extent upon the methods of accounting being used, the amount of data that can readily be obtained from existing records, and the degree of accuracy desired.

STAGE III: DEFINING THE PROBLEM

When the Coordinating Committee has completed the basic fact-gathering studies, outlined in Stage II, it can proceed to use the collected information to define the transportation problem. First, the facts must be consolidated in such a way that they accurately portray the current status of transportation in the community or area. The various blocks of data that were developed in the recommended investigations must be fitted together. On the basis of this integrated body of information, a reliable estimate of future transportation conditions can be made.

Then, by comparing existing and anticipated conditions with appropriate standards, it is possible to determine the extent of deficiencies. The National Committee has formulated a set of recommended standards relating to street and transit service. These yardsticks provide ample latitude for modifications where necessary in light of special local conditions. A resume of the standards, which are presented in full in a procedure manual, is given later in this section.

For this stage, the Coordinating Committee should prepare a work schedule that assigns the several phases to appropriate agencies. The schedule should spell out, for example, who will prepare the various maps, charts, tables, and figures, who will make the estimate of future conditions, who will decide upon the standards, and who will prepare the report summarizing the work.

REVIEW OF EXISTING CONDITIONS

To get a true picture of the quantity and quality of existing transportation, pertinent data from certain of the basic studies must be extracted, collated, and presented in proper form. These studies include land use, origin-destination, street use, traffic service, transit service, physical street system, and financial records. As indicated in Table 2, the rest of the study information will be used for other important phases of the planning program.

Table 2 is a brief description of the presentations and materials which should be developed on the basis of substantive data derived from the individual studies named.

Land Use

It is well known that land use plays a decisive part in molding the traffic patterns of an urban area. Therefore a map of existing land uses should be prepared on the basis of land-use data. The map should show the general distribution of residential, industrial, and commercial activities, as well as the location of schools, parks, boundaries of neighborhoods, and so forth. Topographical features that would affect the location of transportation facilities obviously should be indicated.

Origin and Destination

Based upon the O-D Study, suitable charts or figures should be developed that show the major traffic generators. The charts should indicate the relative number of trips begun in different sections and thus permit a comparison to be made between land use and traffic generation. An illustration is given in Figure 5. This figure, for the City of Albuquerque, New Mexico, reveals that the number one generator of trips in this area is the central business district. It also shows the amount of traffic generated by other sections, such as outlying employment centers and shopping centers. (It is suggested that the largest sections be designated.)

Maps depicting the current pattern of travel also should be made, on the basis both of vehicle trips and of transit riders. A transit-rider map will not be necessary in smaller communities where transit trips are few.

Such maps may be prepared in several ways. A common method is to place so-called "desire

Table 2

HOW BASIC TRANSPORTATION DATA ARE USED IN
DEVELOPING THE PLANNING PROGRAM

Data Obtained From Basic Transportation Studies	Reviewing Existing Conditions	Determining Deficiencies	DEVELOPING THE PLAN		Carrying Out the Plan
			Major Im- provements	Minor Im- provements	
Street use	X	X	X	X	X
Origin-destination	X	X	X	X	X
Land use	X	X	X	X	X
Street service					
Traffic volume	X	X	X	X	X
Travel time	X	X	X		X
Street capacity			X	X	X
Accidents	X	X	X	X	X
Parking	X	X	X	X	X
Control devices				X	X
Transit service					
Routes and coverage	X	X	X	X	X
Transit route inventory				X	X
Passenger load data	X	X	X	X	X
Service frequency				X	X
Transit travel times	X	X	X	X	X
Transit speeds and delays			X	X	X
General operating data			X	X	X
Passenger riding habits			X	X	X
Physical street system	X	X	X	X	X
Financial records	X		X	X	X

lines" on maps (Figure 6). The lines or bands tie together zones between which trips are made, the thickness of the bands indicating the number of trips between zones. This technique is effective for small cities but tends to become confusing when there are a large number of zones.

In the largest cities, it is often advantageous to group zones together into districts on the map and to indicate the desire lines between districts. Supplementary maps may be drawn showing the desire lines of traffic *within* the individual districts. This breakdown of data is useful because it helps to define, on the one hand, over-all need for such facilities as expressways and freeways and, on the other, the smaller problems that will have to be met on a district basis.

Another method employed for large cities is a trip contour map. The urban area is divided into uniform squares and the number of trips which would enter or pass through any particular square

Figure 5

PRINCIPAL TRAFFIC GENERATORS
Albuquerque

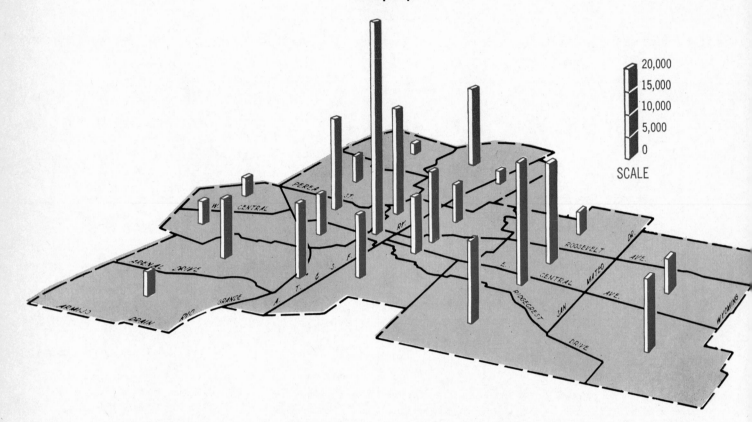

is estimated. Contour lines enclosing squares comparable in desire-line intensity are then drawn for the entire area.

To show data on the composition of urban traffic—also derived from the O-D Study—one of the simplest methods of presentation is in table form (see Tables 3 and 4). Such tables summarize individual trips within the metropolitan area in terms of mode of travel and purpose. They show the relative roles of the various forms of transportation, the purpose of the trips made by different means, and the vehicle mileage registered per day —all essential factors in scaling the transportation problem.

Usually it is also a good idea to prepare a special table, similar to Table 3, for trips made downtown, since this area is often the crux of the traffic problem.

Street Use

A map should be prepared delineating the streets according to their present use. It may be advisable, on the same map, to indicate widths of

paved surface and right of way. Such data would be based on the street inventory.

Traffic Service

In diagnosing traffic service, some of the chief factors that should be weighed are traffic volumes, travel speeds, accidents, and parking.

A volume map depicting the amount of traffic on various streets is useful for picturing the distribution pattern of traffic. The volume data, too, should be summarized in table form to show the vehicle mileage generated on the different street systems. Average auto travel time for particular street segments also should be indicated, preferably on a separate map. Similarly, it may be worth while to show on a map the travel time between origin and destination zones or districts.

Summaries should be made of the accident information collected. The accident rate (on a mileage basis) should be computed for each year, with subtotals according to severity (fatalities, injuries, and property damage). These figures should be plotted and compared with those for previous years to disclose trends.

Collected information on the downtown park-

Figure 6

TRAVEL DESIRES

Internal and External Automobile and Truck Trips Combined, Volume Range of 250 or More in Alexandria, Louisiana

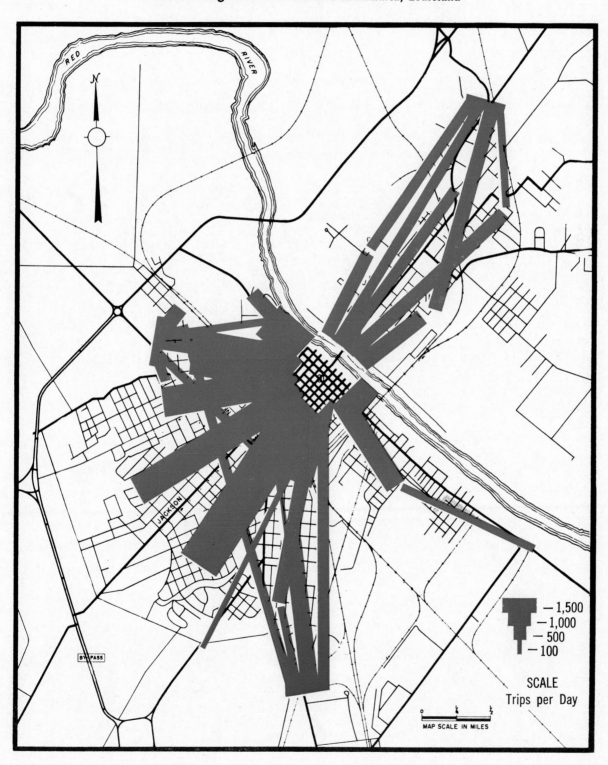

35

Table 3

SUGGESTED SUMMARY TABLE

Vehicle Trips in Average Day

	NO. OF TRIPS	VEHICLE MILES
Auto driver trips	_____	_____
Truck trips	_____	_____
Transit trips	_____	_____
TOTAL	_____	_____

Table 4

SUGGESTED SUMMARY TABLE

Personal Trips According To
Mode of Travel and Trip Purpose

PURPOSE OF TRIP	AUTO DRIVER	AUTO PASSENGER	TRANSIT
Work	_____	_____	_____
Personal business	_____	_____	_____
Social recreation	_____	_____	_____
Shopping	_____	_____	_____
Other	_____	_____	_____
TOTAL	_____	_____	_____

ing supply likewise should be summarized, to show the number of on-street and off-street parking spaces. It is recommended that the total vehicles parked during different hours of the day be computed and plotted on a chart and compared with the available parking supply.

Transit Service

The main points to be presented on transit service relate to route coverage, passenger loading conditions, and transit speeds. For route coverage, maps should be prepared showing the location of routes and the areas that are within convenient walking distances of these routes. A table should be compiled indicating the population within convenient walking distances of the routes.

Similarly, the ratio of seating capacity to loads should be expressed in summary form, as shown in Figure 7. This summary will clearly define the existing load factor on the various transit lines in the community.

Another graphic aid in presenting the transit story is a detailed map showing transit speeds maintained under existing traffic conditions. These speeds also should be reported as a ratio of the speeds obtainable by auto.

Physical Street System

A summary should be made of street conditions. It could include the mileage of streets of various surface types and widths, as well as the mileage that is structurally deficient or unsatisfactory in terms of riding qualities. This information can readily be conveyed in table or map form.

Financial Records

As stated in Stage II, the data concerning current revenues and expenditures for transporta-

Figure 7

HOURLY PASSENGER VOLUME

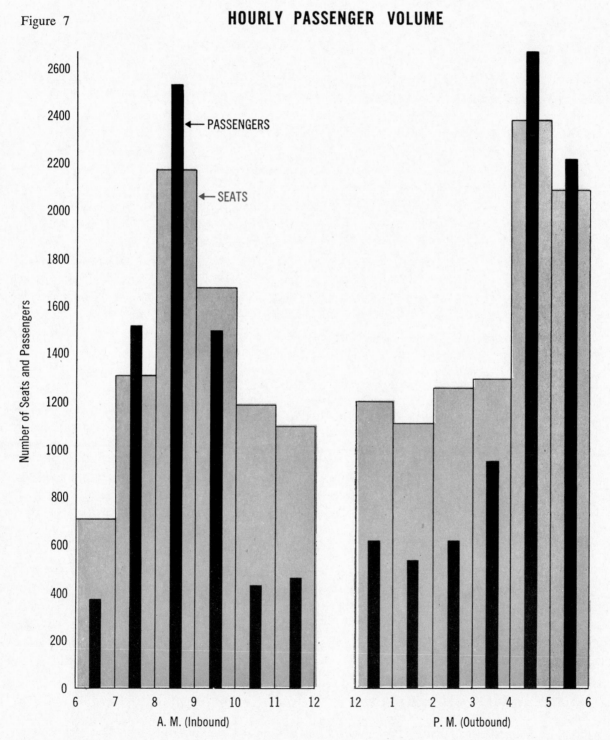

Table 5
SUGGESTED SUMMARY TABLE
Revenues and Nonrevenue Receipts Relating to General Transportation Facilities For Fiscal Year Ended December 31, 19____

REVENUE RECEIPTS

TAXES _____
General property taxes _____
Other taxes _____
Interest and penalties on delinquent taxes _____

TOTAL TAXES _____

LICENSES AND PERMITS
Motor vehicle licenses and fees _____
Other vehicle licenses _____
Curb parking meters _____
Street privileges and permits _____

TOTAL LICENSES AND PERMITS _____

FINES, FORFEITS, AND OTHER PENALTIES
Traffic fines _____
Forfeits _____

TOTAL FINES, FORFEITS, AND OTHER PENALTIES _____

REVENUE FROM USE OF MONEY AND PROPERTY
Interest on bank deposits _____
Interest on investments _____
Rents and concessions _____
Royalties _____

TOTAL REVENUE FROM USE OF MONEY AND PROPERTY _____

REVENUE FROM OTHER AGENCIES
Gasoline and other motor fuel taxes shared with the state _____
Motor vehicle licenses shared with the state _____
State grants in aid for highways _____
Grants and contributions received for streets and highways _____

TOTAL REVENUE FROM OTHER AGENCIES _____

CHARGES FOR CURRENT SERVICES
Street and sidewalk assessments _____
Street lighting rates or charges _____
Street sanitation rates or charges _____
Bridge and tunnel tolls _____
TOTAL CHARGES FOR CURRENT SERVICES _____
OTHER REVENUES _____

TOTAL REVENUE RECEIPTS _____

NONREVENUE RECEIPTS

BORROWINGS
Sales of bonds _____
Sales of notes _____

TOTAL BORROWINGS _____

Sale and compensation for loss of fixed assets _____

TOTAL NONREVENUE RECEIPTS _____

38

Table 6
SUGGESTED SUMMARY TABLE
Direct Expenditures on General Transportation Facilities
Fiscal Year ended December 31, 19_____

DESCRIPTION	EXPRESSWAYS		MAJOR ARTERIALS		COLLECTOR STREETS	LOCAL STREETS
	State	Local	State	Local		
OPERATION AND MAINTENANCE:						
Federal						
State						
County						
City						
Other						
TOTAL						
CAPITAL OUTLAYS:						
Federal						
State						
County						
City						
Other						
TOTAL						
TOTAL DIRECT EXPENDITURES						

tion facilities should be tabulated to present the existing pattern in concise form. (See Tables 5 and 6.) This record, compiled annually, will, over a period of years, reveal any developing trends. Such information is useful to determine potentials in the various revenue areas. Projections of future income can be made by using the tax bases for existing revenues.

PROJECTING FUTURE TRAVEL

With existing conditions evaluated, future traffic demands must be considered, for both must be taken into account if maximum benefits are to be realized from transportation improvements.

As in any other area of forecast, the projection of travel patterns is at best only a reasonable estimate of what the future has in store. Since urban traffic patterns are influenced by so many factors—land development, population, cost and quality of various forms of transportation, economic status of population, hours of work, recreation, social habits, and shopping patterns—the task is by no means simple.

However, research has indicated that travel patterns are mainly governed by three things—land-use distribution, transportation facilities, and living habits; and further, that these factors are interrelated. For example, the presence of an expressway or rapid transit line will have a perceptible impact on the land-use patterns and living habits in the immediate vicinity. An attempt should therefore be made to give due weighting to

In planning transportation facilities, it is necessary to analyze traffic patterns in order to forecast where and when people will be traveling in the future. Taking account of these anticipated traffic demands serves to insure a maximum return on improvements.

the reciprocal impact of these factors on one another for the time span covered by the projection.

Land-Use Distribution

The distribution of land use controls the origin and destination of a large portion of trips. The residences of the people dictate the starting points of much of the daily travel. Similarly, the destinations of many trips are controlled by the location of employment, shopping, cultural, and recreational areas. In turn, the location of these land uses is influenced strongly by transportation facilities.

Unfortunately, in the past there has been little effort to integrate land-use planning with transportation planning, with the result that seldom has either produced sound plans. A program to insure this essential coordination is outlined in a procedure manual. In carrying out each of the suggested steps, over-all community objectives should always be kept in mind.

What type of residential areas does the community want to develop? Is the city interested in preserving the strength of the downtown area? Should land be set aside for attracting new industries? What amenities in the area must be preserved? Such questions should be evaluated by each community. Whatever the fundamental goals of the community, they should be reflected in the land-use plan—which in turn is the main basis for projecting future travel.

Transportation Facilities

A second important factor affecting travel patterns is transportation facilities. Highway development, transit improvements, and car ownership all come under this heading.

Numerous origin-destination studies have demonstrated that car ownership per family is directly related to the frequency of trips made by the family, the mode of travel used, and the purpose of the trips. Thus, the anticipated doubling of car ownership in urban areas within the next 20 years is going to have a great impact on travel trends. Consequently, a careful projection of future car ownership should be made.

Living Habits

Virtually all predictions of future living habits in the United States anticipate fewer working hours and more leisure time. Yet most authorities doubt that reduction of working hours will have much effect upon daily peak travel patterns. Neither a 7-hour workday nor a 4-day week, with more vacation time, would substantially change the existing pattern of peak hours. On the other hand, the increase in leisure time will definitely boost recreational travel. Such factors should be considered in trying to assess the impact of living habits on future travel patterns.

Projection Procedure

The first step in forecasting travel patterns is to estimate the effect that living habits and transportation facilities will have on the frequency of trips, the purpose of trips, and the mode of travel that will be used. This estimate can be made through a special analysis of the O-D data, as out-

Table 7
PROJECTED TRAVEL

	Number of Trips		Vehicle or Passenger Miles	
	1955	1975	1955	1975
Auto driver trips				
Truck trips				
Transit trips				
TOTAL				

lined in a procedure manual. Then on the basis of these findings and of known traffic-generating characteristics of various land uses, the number of trips that will be produced by given land uses in the future should be determined. This accomplished, the trips should be distributed throughout the urban area in accordance with established principles of traffic attraction.

In presenting the projection data, charts and maps should be developed similar to those prepared on the O-D information. Particularly useful is a table, such as Table 7, concisely showing the expected growth of the traffic problem.

ADOPTING STANDARDS

Before the Coordinating Committee can measure present and future transportation deficiencies, it must adopt a set of standards by which to evaluate existing and future transportation service. These standards can also serve as a guide when developing a master transportation plan. Moreover, these standards can be helpful in the design, maintenance, and operation of the various transportation facilities.

Following is a summary of the standards and guides recommended by the National Committee on Urban Transportation. They are divided into two parts, the first relating to the street system and its service, and the second to transit service.

Standards for Street Facilities and Services

In urban areas, street design is influenced considerably by topography, population density, land development, vehicle characteristics, the character and composition of traffic movement, present and future traffic volumes, and cost of construction. The quality and quantity of service required depend upon the desires and needs of individual auto, truck, and transit users, the size of the city, land use, over-all city planning objectives, and economic factors.

The impact of these controlling factors must be considered in the development of suitable service and design standards. Therefore, in formulating the standards set forth here, the influence of these factors has been evaluated in light of the best available city planning criteria and engineering knowledge and practice. Since the standards reflect typical aspects of urban areas, modification may be necessary in some cases to allow for unusual local conditions.

The criteria employed to appraise service and

guide design are based upon the following general premises:

1. To develop good street transportation adequately serving various land uses and to insure logical community development, it is desirable to establish a network of streets divided into systems, each system accommodating either movement and/or access to a varying, but distinctively different, degree.

2. The purpose of each street system must govern the selection of the structural features, the visible dimensions of streets, and the use of any control devices or measures, in order that the basic service of each system may be maintained and improved.

3. Terminal facilities which include any space, area, structure, or appurtenance, either on or off the streets, used for the parking of vehicles and the loading or unloading of persons or goods, are an integral part of street transportation, and must be considered in providing satisfactory service.

Accordingly, the street classification plan or master street plan which the city ultimately develops should designate all existing and proposed streets into systems, each having a specific transportation function to perform.

Criteria for Establishing Systems

The principal factors to be considered in designating streets into appropriate systems are the travel desires of auto, truck and transit users; the access needs of adjacent land development; the network pattern of existing streets; and existing and proposed land uses. But before this designation can be made a thorough understanding of the function of each street must be established. These, briefly, are the characteristics and functions of four basic categories of streets:

EXPRESSWAYS—The function of the urban expressway is to expedite movement of all types of traffic (automobiles, transit vehicles, and trucks) between distant points in a community or metropolitan area. By removing through traffic from other parts of the street system, it enables all streets to perform their roles more effectively. In order to insure safe and expeditious service for heavy traffic volumes, expressway design should include full control of access.

A complete system of these high-type facilities should afford express service between large residential areas, employment centers, and the business district. It should also integrate principal rural highways.

Figure 8

EXPRESSWAY AND MAJOR ARTERIAL SYSTEMS
San Diego (Population: 435,000)

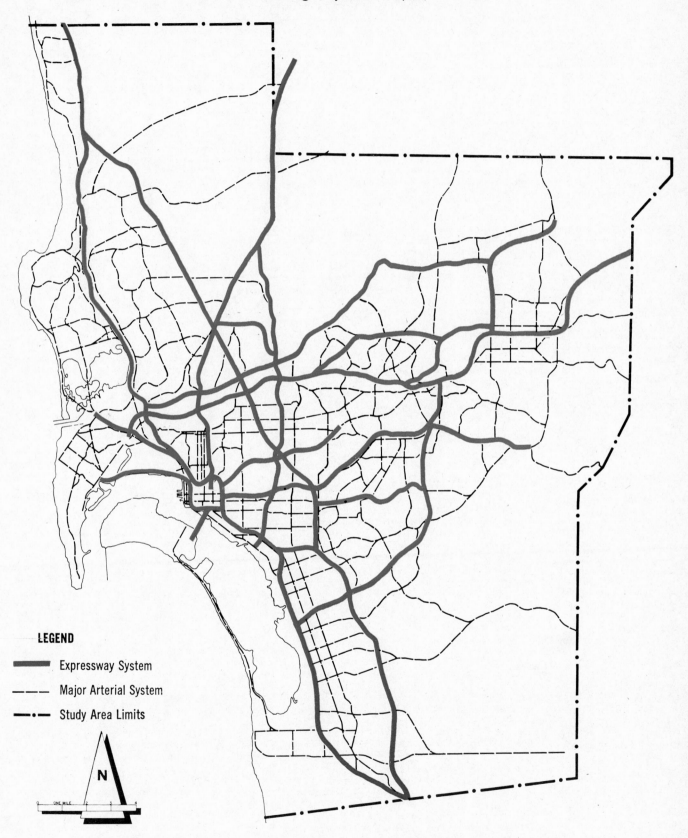

LEGEND

━━━ Expressway System

--- Major Arterial System

-·-·- Study Area Limits

N

ONE MILE

Expressways should be so located that they do not disrupt sound land-use development. Often expressway components can be placed in such a way as to form boundaries between different land uses. Residential areas may thus be insulated from industrial sites, for instance.

Spacing of expressways is contingent upon traffic volume, street deficiencies, transit service, location of major traffic generators, topographical conditions, and many other factors. Nevertheless many studies have shown that expressways should be spaced at intervals up to five miles—one or two miles near the heart of the city, and three to five miles in the suburban sections.

The expressway system of San Diego, California (Figure 8), partially completed, is a typical example. Important rural highways are interconnected to provide fast, convenient intercity movement. A circumferential route around the central business district will provide circulation and access to the area without requiring through traffic to penetrate the core of the central area. Radial routes leading from the inner loop to the other areas of traffic generation are interconnected by crosstown and other circumferential routes.

A radial pattern of expressways has certain limitations in that it tends to force traffic to use the downtown loop. A grid pattern, on the other hand, distributes traffic more evenly throughout the system. Consequently, some of the more recent expressway systems have a gridiron appearance.

In smaller cities the chief difficulty may be in accommodating through travel. Some communities have met this problem by building one or two express routes. The expressway system of Colorado Springs, Colorado, provides convenient movement for intercity travel and, at the same time, gives traffic relief to critical sections of the major street system (Figure 9). It also ties together the downtown area and the large industrial sections of the community.

MAJOR ARTERIAL SYSTEM—This system, together with expressways (where they exist), must serve as the principal network for through traffic flow. Therefore major arterial streets should connect areas of principal traffic generation and important rural highways entering the city. These streets should be coordinated with existing and proposed expressway systems to provide for distribution and collection of through traffic to and from collector and local street systems.

A properly designated and developed major arterial system should help to define residential neighborhoods, industrial sites, and commercial areas and to minimize conflicts with school and park developments. To provide sufficient capacity and the desired quality of service, major arterial streets should not be more than one mile apart.

COLLECTOR STREET SYSTEM—This system includes all distributor and collector streets serving traffic between major arterials and local streets, and also those streets used mainly for traffic movement within residential, commercial, and industrial areas. They may also serve to connect adjacent neighborhoods.

Continuity of the collector street pattern is necessary if various areas are to be fully interconnected. In order to accommodate local movement, distribute traffic effectively, and provide sufficient capacity, the major street and collector systems combined should form a network of streets spaced about one-half mile apart. This network will be ample to permit adequate transit coverage of such areas.

LOCAL STREET SYSTEM—Included in this system are all streets used primarily for direct access to residential, commercial, industrial, or other abutting property. Continuity of the street system in residential areas is not important. It should provide easy access to adjacent property and connect with collector or major arterial streets. All through-traffic movement should be discouraged on local streets.

Because, in older sections of the community, many local streets are of considerable length, there has been a tendency for them to be preempted by through traffic. However, when all streets are properly classified and then developed in accordance with their primary purpose, the longer local streets will be divided into shorter sections by collectors. This division will allow the local streets to serve their main purpose of providing access to residences, business establishments, and industries.

Balanced Street System

To have an efficient street system there must be a proper balance between the various types of streets—expressways, major arterials, collector streets, and local streets. If there are too many miles of major arterial streets, for example, the cost of improvement may be excessive. At the same time, proper balance helps to preserve the amenities of different land uses, particularly in residential areas where the classification scheme reduces the amount of through traffic and thus pre-

Figure 9

STREET SYSTEMS
Colorado Springs (Population: 65,000)

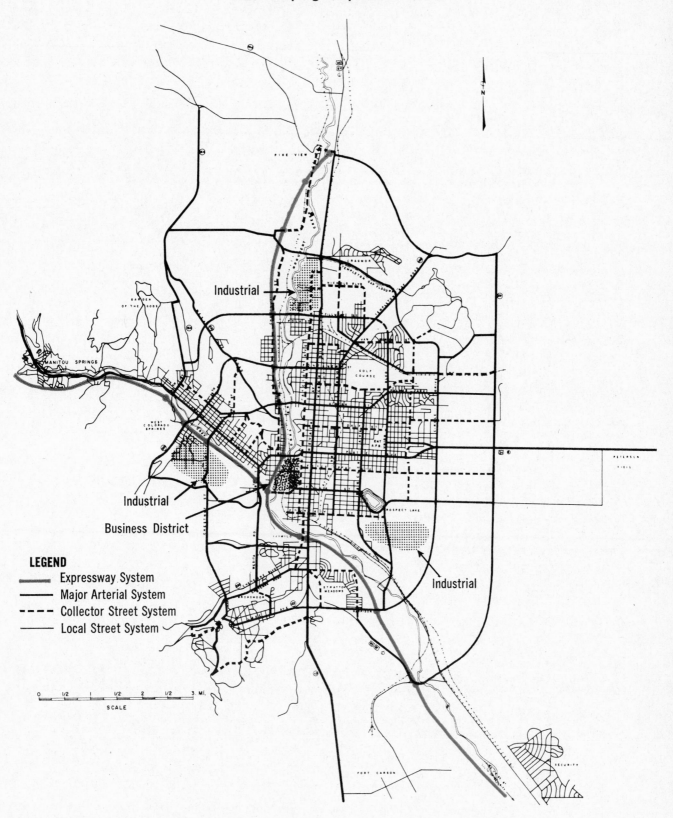

Industrial

Industrial

Business District

Industrial

LEGEND
- Expressway System
- Major Arterial System
- Collector Street System
- Local Street System

SCALE

A sound street plan calls for proper integration of the four basic classes of streets. Note in this scene how the major arterial (vertical in photo) is linked with the expressway and also connects with collector streets. The latter provide access to the local streets.

serves land values and provides greater safety to residents.

Based upon past studies, the breakdown of street use set forth in Table 8 is suggested as a guide in evaluating present street use and in developing a master street plan for communities of various sizes.

The percentages suggested are typical of the classification plan that can be established in conformance with the street patterns found in most cities today.

Evaluation of Street Service

The level of service that a street system provides depends upon how well each street is performing its primary purpose. The degree to which any system fulfills its basic purpose hinges directly on its operational characteristics and design. The highest quality of service will be obtained when there is complete compatibility between these factors and the purpose of the system.

Generally speaking, the purpose of the system reflects whether speed of movement or direct access to property is the main service requirement. The desired quality of movement or access achieved must be obtained with maximum safety. Accident rates are an index of safety.

Criteria are set forth below to evaluate the performance of each street in light of all these factors. Other criteria are given to measure the efficiency of the whole street network on another basis—namely, over-all travel time for trips of various lengths.

Expressway System

In addition to handling extraordinary traffic volumes with a high degree of safety, expressway systems are expected to meet the travel-time desires of users more adequately than other systems.

Table 8
SUGGESTED DIVISION OF STREET MILEAGE

Population of Metropolitan Areas	PERCENTAGE OF MILEAGE IN EACH SYSTEM		
	Expressways*	Major Arterial and Collector Streets	Local
Under 25,000	*	25-35	65-75
25,000 to 150,000	*	20-30	70-80
150,000 to 500,000	2-4	20-25	75-80
Over 500,000	4-6	15-20	75-80

* Depends on through traffic needs.

Over-all speeds of from 35 to 50 miles per hour should be possible, and minimum over-all speeds of 35 miles per hour should be obtained at peak periods of traffic flow (Table 9).

The accident rates shown in Table 9 illustrate the degree of safety now obtained on some expressway systems. The values given are intended merely as a guide to the relative safety of travel and should not be construed as the ultimate goal or standard.

In recognition of the vital role of transit in urban areas, and the need for its efficiency as a transportation medium, transit operations—rail or rubber tired, as appropriate to particular needs—must be given due consideration in the design of new expressways and in the operation of existing high-type facilities. If transit vehicles are making stops on the expressway, or if it is anticipated that transit will desire to make stops, special loading bays with adequate merging lanes should be provided. In cases where transit volumes are exceedingly heavy, it may be advisable to provide lanes exclusively for transit.

Major Arterial System

In most cities, if the major arterial system is to furnish adequate service, it should be possible to maintain on it over-all speeds ranging from 25 to 35 miles per hour. During peak traffic flow, over-all speeds approaching 25 miles per hour should be obtainable (Table 9).

A secondary purpose of the major arterial system is to provide some degree of direct access to abutting property. The use of the curb lane for parking or for loading and unloading of goods should be permitted only if the desired speed on these streets can be maintained.

Since this system accommodates the routes for transit service, provision should be made for the loading and unloading of passengers. The requirements for bus stops are dealt with in a procedure manual.

The accident rates on major arterial streets should not exceed the values given in Table 9. These values represent the accident experience on some of the safer major arterial street systems.

Collector Street System

Collector streets serve a dual purpose by providing a means for local through-traffic movement within an area and direct access to abutting property. Hence provision should be made to accommodate turning movements, parking, and loading and unloading of people and goods. In line with these activities, over-all speeds on the collector street system should range from 20 to 25 miles per hour.

Since this system serves certain transit routes, provision also should be made for the loading and unloading of passengers. The requirements for bus stops are covered in the procedure manual.

Accident rates on collector streets should not exceed those given in Table 9. Again, these rates should be viewed as a guide to safety evaluation, and not as the ultimate goal.

Local Street System

Since the main service objective of local streets is to afford access to abutting property, over-all speeds should be low in order to permit frequent

Table 9
MINIMUM DESIRABLE OPERATING CHARACTERISTICS
OF EXISTING STREETS

TYPE OF STREET	Overall Speed		Accident Rates per 100 Million Vehicle Miles	
	Peak Hour	Off Peak	Fatal	Injury
Expressway:				
1. Full control	35	35-50	1.5-2.0	50-60
2. Partial control	35	35-50	2.0-3.0	60-100
Major Arterial:				
1. Divided	25	25-35	2.0-5.0	75-150
2. Undivided	25	25-35	3.0-6.0	100-200
Collector:	20	20-25	2.0-4.0	60-80
Local:				
1. Business	10	10-20	0.0-1.0	5.0-20
2. Industrial	10	10-20	0.0-1.0	1.0-20
3. Residential	10	10-20	0.0-1.0	0.5-10

stops and turning movements with maximum safety. This factor applies whether the streets serve residences, business, or other land uses. Because these routes are used only for short distances, over-all speeds of from 10 to 20 miles per hour are compatible with service needs.

Loading, unloading, and access being major service functions of local streets, liberal use of curb space should be allowed where possible. Proper location and design of driveways, entrances, and exits are essential to insure safe and efficient access.

Accident rates on local streets should not exceed the values given in Table 9. These rates represent the best that are available to date and should be used as a guide in appraising safety.

Efficiency of Street Systems

To measure street efficiency, it is recommended that automobile travel time be determined between zones or districts used in the Origin-Destination Study. This speed can be calculated from running times obtained for the major arterial streets. By comparing travel time (on an airline basis), it is possible to evaluate speed of service, as well as the efficiency of the street pattern.

Studies have shown that as trips grow longer, over-all travel time becomes increasingly important as a measure of efficiency. The travel time for trips of various lengths shown in Table 10 should be obtainable for 85 per cent of the trips made during an average weekday peak hour. The table is based upon the service potential of a well-balanced street system, in which each street operates in line with its principal function.

The figures in Table 10 are the recommended standard for over-all automobile travel time for trips of various lengths. It is well recognized that buses operating on a street system cannot obtain these speeds. Generally, however, transit speeds

Table 10

MINIMUM DESIRABLE AUTO TRAVEL TIME FOR TRIPS OF VARIOUS LENGTHS
Measured on the Basis of Airline Distance

AVERAGE WEEKDAY PEAK HOUR

Length of Trip	Travel Time
2 miles	7 minutes
4 miles	12 minutes
6 miles	16 minutes
8 miles	20 minutes
10 miles	24 minutes
12 miles	28 minutes

of between 70 and 80 per cent of automobile speeds can be obtained. Whether they are achieved will depend upon local conditions and policies, such as the frequency of stops, adequacy of loading areas, and the street pattern itself. It is recommended that each city make a comparison between auto speeds and transit speeds and, in light of these conditions, determine an appropriate transit standard.

Any street system should be operated to permit reasonable speeds and at the same time afford adequate safety. If local conditions are normal, the fatality rate should not exceed 4 deaths per 100 million vehicle miles. The injury rate should be kept below 100 injuries per 100 million vehicle miles.

Traffic Control Devices and Measures

Maximum efficiency and safety in the use of streets can be obtained only with the employment of the most advanced traffic control devices and measures. All users of the street network—motorists, transit and truck operators, and pedestrians—must be informed, guided, and directed to insure greatest convenience and safety. Application of the right control measures, devices, and traffic engineering techniques, so that each system will better perform its primary purpose, will help to accomplish these goals. In other words, the control devices and measures should be geared to the specific needs of the various classes of streets—expressways, major arterials, collectors, and local streets.

One of the most effective control measures is the use of one-way streets. This technique generally helps to increase travel speeds and reduce accidents, thus improving the efficiency of the street system. The use of transit lanes or even transit streets appears to offer much hope in providing freer movement for both transit and automobiles. Control of curb parking, too, can increase the efficiency of all forms of street transportation.

Pedestrian Service

The downtown area often is the scene of conflicts between pedestrians and vehicles. A basic rule for remedying this situation is to give priority to pedestrian traffic on local streets and to vehicular movement on arterial streets. On wide streets, safety islands or median strips should be constructed to increase the safety of walkers in crossing. Special pedestrian signals also should be considered.

In the development of subdivision areas, convenient pedestrian access ways are needed to permit transit patrons to reach bus stops without using circuitous routes. Similarly, convenient pedestrian access should be provided to schools and local shopping areas.

There should be sidewalks on both sides of the street in most residential areas. Sidewalk requirements will depend upon the volume of pedestrian and vehicular traffic and the need for play space. Where both pedestrian and vehicle volumes are low, sidewalks may not be necessary. In all retail areas, sidewalks at least 10 feet wide are required to handle pedestrian traffic.

Structural Conditions

Streets in urban areas should be capable of withstanding heavy traffic use over long periods with minimum maintenance. All urban streets should have a hard, dustless surface free of holes, ruts, or other evidence of structural failure. When frequent resurfacing or patching operations are necessary to maintain a good riding pavement, traffic movements are disrupted and higher overall costs may result. The goal of all structural improvements should be to obtain lowest annual cost when all factors are considered—traffic delays, maintenance and construction costs, and so forth.

Terminal Facilities

Terminal facilities for parking and for the loading and unloading of people and goods are an intrinsic part of street transportation. Efficient movement and adequate facilities for vehicles at rest are, in fact, the two sides of the same coin.

Curb Spaces

Nevertheless, from the standpoint of traffic regulation, the movement of cars, public transit vehicles, and trucks must be given preference over the need for parking and the loading and unloading of goods at the curb. The quality of movement —as reflected in over-all speeds of both automobiles and public transit—need not exceed the values set forth above for each street system (Table 9). Within these limits, the use of curb space, on those systems having a direct access function, should be allocated in the following order of preference: (1) loading and unloading of persons; (2) loading and unloading of goods; (3) parking.

Off-Street Terminal Facilities

In planning and developing off-street parking and loading facilities, the capacity and operation of these units must be related to the traffic-moving capabilities of the street on which they are located. Off-street facilities should be so developed and regulated that they will not reduce the service of adjacent streets below the standards for movement already set forth (Table 9). A more detailed discussion of standards pertaining to commercial loading terminals, transit terminals, and off-street parking facilities will be found in the procedure manuals.

Geometric Design

Correction of deficiencies in the geometric design of highways is much more difficult and costly in urban than in rural areas. As a rule, space for increasing the surface width or changing other design features is seriously limited by commercial, industrial, or other urban land developments. It is most important to provide proper width, grade, curvature, sight distance, and other geometric elements in all new construction.

The characteristics of geometric design should in every case conform to the purpose of the particular street system. Standards for geometric design are spelled out in precise terms in a manual on that subject. These standards cover lane width, curb design, shoulders, medians, number of lanes, right-of-way, design speed, sight distances, curvature, grades, and other design features (See Summary Table 11).

Table 11
SUMMARY OF MINIMUM DESIGN STANDARDS FOR URBAN STREETS

Design Elements (All widths in feet)	Expressway	Major Arterial	COLLECTOR STREET		LOCAL STREET	
			Single Family Residential Area	Other	Single Family Residential Area	Other
Number of traffic lanes	4 up	4-6	2	4	2	2-4
Width of traffic lanes	12	11	10	11	10	11
Width of curb parking lane or shoulder	10	10	10	10	8*	10
Width of border area	16	12	10	8	10	8
Median width	20	12	—	—	—	—
Width of right-of-way	120 up	100-120	60	80	50-60	60-80

Under light traffic conditions, parking may be limited to one side.

Standards for Transit Services

In setting forth the general standards and guides for transit services, it is recognized that these yardsticks must be related to the economic feasibility of providing service. Cities cannot expect public transit to operate "in the red" in supplying service which the communities deem essential—unless they are willing to subsidize this service to the extent necessary. The following set of standards is predicated on the assumption that service standards and facilities are in line with public demands and interests—and are, at the same time, economically justified. Standards or warrants should be such that they will not cause any transit operation to risk its financial stability. Unless financial solvency is maintained, transit service is bound to deteriorate.

Routing

Transit routes should be laid out to provide maximum service to the community as a whole. Transit should be conceived on a systemwide basis, but in the development of individual routes the following considerations are important:

1. The route should be direct with respect to origins and destinations of passengers. (Transfers which riders must make should be held to a minimum.)

2. Routes should be free of duplication except where they converge.

3. In built-up areas, routes should be spaced at approximately half-mile intervals (quarter-mile walking distance) with intervals increased proportionately in areas of medium and low population density.

4. Routes should include a minimum number of turning movements, and should have adequate provision for turn-around at both ends and for layover at one or both ends.

5. Routes should have reasonable long-term flexibility (not necessarily day-to-day flexibility), to meet changing conditions.

6. Routes should be laid out to take full advantage of street characteristics and possible operational improvements. Such factors include the condition and type of roadways utilized, design features, traffic control measures, strength of roadway structure (especially at vehicle stops), width, surface, control of access from side streets, and provisions for loading and unloading.

In adjusting present routes and developing new ones, the convenience and comfort of passengers should be a prime consideration. Improvement of transit speed is of the utmost importance. Speed often can be stepped up by selecting routes which have desirable physical characteristics and on which advantageous parking and traffic control measures can be adopted.

Loading

Loading standards must be conceived in light of the revenues derived from and the cost of operation. Though every effort should be made to avoid crowding of passengers and to reduce standing to a minimum, the load factor must be in line with the willingness of the public to pay for superior service. It is hoped that ultimately standards of 135 per cent or 125 per cent in peak hours may

Quality of transit service is generally gauged by loading standards, which relate number of passengers to seating capacity. Standards should reflect both the desires of riders and the cost of operation.

be obtainable. On the basis of existing fare structures and facilities, however, the maximum number of passengers averaged over a 30-minute period, passing any point along a route, should not exceed the following percentages of the designated seating capacity of the vehicle:

- Base or nonrush periods   100 per cent
- Transition periods   125 per cent
- Peak or rush-hour periods   150 per cent

Frequency of Service

The question of standards for frequency of service hinges chiefly on two widely differing conditions—one, transit routes that serve large volumes of passenger traffic; and the other, routes that serve very small volumes.

In the first case, service should be frequent

enough to provide a sufficient number of vehicles passing the maximum load point to handle riders in accordance with the loading standards set forth above.

Requirements for transit service in small-volume areas are generally so vague and ill defined that it is difficult to establish standards. There is ample evidence, however, that here it is not so much the frequency of service as the proper *timing* of service that is important.

Frequency of Transit Stops

Experience in local surface transit operations proves the desirability of adopting the following standards on frequency of stops:

In ordinary residential areas, the number of local surface transit stops should not exceed seven per mile.

In commercial and industrial areas, the number and location of local surface transit stops should be determined in each case by (1) the character of commercial or industrial development and (2) concentrations of people and their demonstrated dependence upon transit services.

In crowded downtown areas where stops of several transit routes are concentrated on a few major streets, consideration should be given to the possibility of alternate stops for the several routes.

Transit Speed

Because of the wide variations in traffic volume, traffic and parking control, street widths and layouts, and other controlling factors, a standard for scheduled speed in miles per hour for use in all cities is not practical.

Therefore it is suggested that the operating speeds in each community be evaluated in terms of the ratio between average transit speeds and average automobile speeds. A comparison can then be made between this ratio for the entire community and the one developed for the particular route under consideration. If the second ratio is lower, a further investigation should be made of the route to find out if this slower operation is due to particular characteristics of the route.

The ultimate aim should be to operate schedule speeds approaching the following standards:

a. Local service—15 miles per hour

b. Express service on arterial streets—20 to 25 miles per hour

c. Express service on expressways—35 to 40 miles per hour

Adherence to Schedule

It is difficult to set a firm standard for adherence to schedule, since traffic congestion and other variable factors external to the public transit operation have a great effect upon performance. If and when such a standard can be devised, it may be expressed as a "percentage of operations *on time*." Meanwhile, it is recommended that the following tentative standards be used under normal conditions:

Base and night hours—90 per cent or better "on time"

Pre-peak, peak, and post-peak hours—70 per cent or better "on time"

Extensions into New Areas

The passenger revenue estimated to be produced by a new or extended service should equal or exceed the estimated out-of-pocket cost of operation of the extension in order to warrant a 90-day "terminable" trial. To justify continuation of the extension, the actual passenger revenue produced in the last 30 days of the trial period must equal or exceed the actual out-of-pocket operating cost. (These costs are spelled out in a standards manual.)

Curtailment or Abandonment of Service

The actual passenger revenue attributable to an existing service must equal or exceed the actual out-of-pocket cost of rendering that service; otherwise, such service should either be curtailed to bring the cost of operation within the scope of the revenue, or abandoned if excessive financial loss occurs. The only exceptions are when operating performance of the remainder of the system demonstrates that it can "carry" the losing route without impairment of the financial position of the company; or when the community wishes to subsidize the company to offset its losses on the route in question, if continued operation is insisted upon by the regulatory authority.

DETERMINING PRESENT AND FUTURE DEFICIENCIES

The point has now been reached in the planning program where practical appraisal of present and future deficiencies in the street system and evaluation of transit service can be made.

When the essential facts have been organized and properly presented, and the recommended standards reviewed, the next step is to apply the standards. Comparison of the present status of transportation in the community with adopted standards will provide direct indications of the nature and size of existing deficiencies. Projection of the current deficiencies, in terms of the developed estimates of future conditions, will provide a valid picture of long-term requirements.

Appraising Street Pattern and Use

In reviewing the street system in light of the standards, the map that was prepared to show the type of use should be studied. The percentage of street mileage in various classes—expressway, major arterial, collector, and local—should be compared with the standards. On the basis of this comparison and the standards for spacing various types of streets, it should be fairly easy to locate on the map the areas where there is over- or under-concentration of certain types of street use.

In addition, the use of streets should be evaluated in terms of the impact on community development. Are the major arterial streets and expressways adequately serving the chief commercial and industrial areas, and also the outlying residential developments? Is there a sufficient number of collectors to handle the distribution of traffic to various areas? Do the arterial streets create accident hazards in the vicinity of neighborhood schools, parks, and playgrounds? Do arterials cut through neighborhoods in a way that impairs the physical integrity or the social amenities of these areas? By objectively considering such questions, the major weaknesses of the present street plant can be brought into focus.

These findings on street pattern and use will provide the foundation for the street classification plan.

Evaluation of Street Service

The process of determining deficiencies in street service has two broad aspects. One is consideration of the main characteristics of individual streets. The second is concerned with the efficiency of the street system as a whole.

Service of Individual Street

Since the service of the street system is really a reflection of the performance of individual streets, a step-by-step analysis should be made of each street to see how effectively it carries out its role. In line with the standards, every street should be checked in terms of (1) travel speed, (2) accident rate, and (3) structural condition.

In the Traffic Service Study, over-all speed determinations were developed and subsequently reported on an individual street basis. These should now be compared with the standard for particular types of streets. The below-standard streets should be indicated on a map to depict the areas where travel speed deficiencies occur. This information, along with the other indexes used in the individual street analysis, may point to specific remedies—removal of parking, widening of a street, elimination of a jog, or building of a new bridge or expressway.

Accident experience is another important factor to be considered in evaluating the service of the street system. It is advisable to develop accident rates individually for the more important major arterial streets and expressways. A sufficient number of accident reports should be available for each such street to insure the statistical stability of the rates established. This information will reveal the streets with the worst accident experience, and these should be portrayed on a map.

Using the yardsticks given in the Standards section, a general inventory of structural deficiencies should be prepared. This may take the form of a table listing mileage of unsurfaced streets, streets having unsatisfactory riding quality, and streets showing excessive maintenance costs or need of reconstruction.

An estimate of anticipated structural requirements should then be prepared. For the immediate future, this estimate can be done reasonably well on the basis of the structural life expectancies established for existing facilities in the street inventory. However, beyond 10 years or so, structural needs should be determined from known patterns of structural life expectancy. Replacement of new facilities should be figured on the same basis. This information should be summarized in table form.

Efficiency of Street System

As was indicated in the Standards section, there are two basic tests of efficiency of a street system: (1) over-all speed and (2) over-all accident rate.

With the collected information about relative speeds on various segments of the major street system, it is possible to evaluate over-all automobile speed for trips of different lengths. This evaluation is made by comparing the travel time between origin-destination zones or districts and the standards. Findings can be shown by means either of a table or of a map. Such a map, for San Diego, California, is shown in Figure 10. This map highlights the movements in the metropolitan area

Figure 10

DESIRE LINE MAP — STREET DEFICIENCIES

San Diego Metropolitan Area

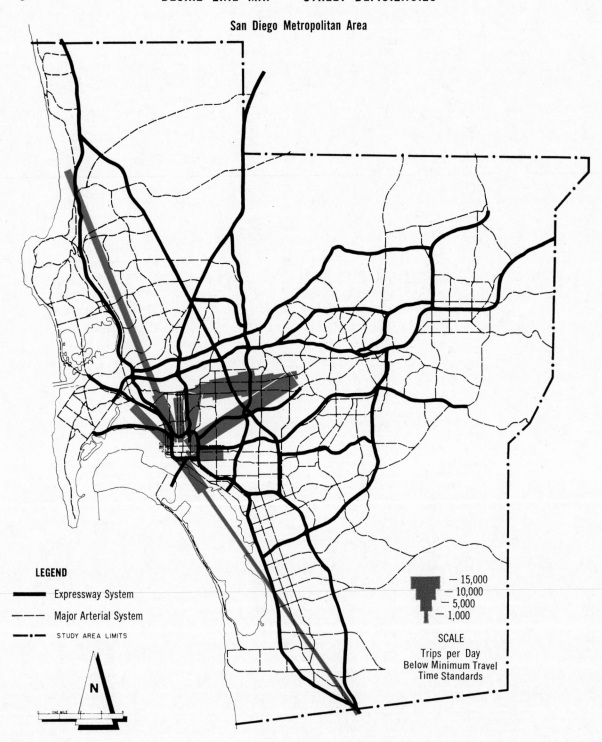

LEGEND

━━━━━ Expressway System

─ ─ ─ ─ Major Arterial System

─ ·· ─ ·· ─ STUDY AREA LIMITS

N

ONE MILE

— 15,000
— 10,000
— 5,000
— 1,000

SCALE
Trips per Day
Below Minimum Travel
Time Standards

54

which are below standard rather than where such movements occur. (Speed on individual streets will indicate *where*.) This information of course will be valuable in designating the location of needed transportation facilities.

A map similar to Figure 10 should be prepared to indicate future deficiencies in travel time. Naturally the map should reflect projected O-D volumes. Travel times between O-D zones or districts should be estimated on the basis of the anticipated volumes and the observed relation between speeds and volumes on the existing street system. On the other hand, since this method requires a fund of information on traffic speed relations which some cities may not have, future street deficiencies may have to be estimated in another way. The deficiencies can be portrayed simply by comparing anticipated traffic volumes with the capacity of the street system.

Terminal Facilities

Development of terminal facilities must be viewed in terms of the moving traffic that must be accommodated on the street system. Is available curb space allocated in the recommended order of preference, namely: (1) loading and unloading of people, (2) loading and unloading of goods, and (3) parking? Do the bus stops meet the specifications set forth in the procedure manual? Are loading zones adequate in size and properly located? Are off-street parking facilities located so as not to overtax the capacity of major streets? Have all off-street parking needs been met which it is economically feasible to supply?

On the basis of projected O-D data, an estimate of future off-street parking needs should be made for the largest traffic generator.

Evaluation of Transit Service

In analyzing travel time patterns, a separate analysis should be made of transit movement. In this case the zone-to-zone speeds should be represented as a percentage of auto speeds between zones. After establishing the median percentage between transit and automobile speeds, it is a simple matter to pick out the areas that have the slowest service. Routes in these areas should then be individually examined by conducting speed and delay studies, thus revealing the causes of their sub-par performance—causes which often include traffic congestion, curb parking, and ineffective control measures or inadequate enforcement of controls.

In addition to considering transit speed, a comparison should be made of present transit system coverage with the suggested standards. This comparison can be shown graphically by means of a map similar to that shown in Figure 4. It is also recommended that the percentage of transit coverage be determined for built-up residential developments in the metropolitan area and that these figures be compared with the standards. Transit routes also should be checked with school locations, industrial areas, shopping centers, and other areas of concentration to gauge the coverage of these areas.

The load factor should be determined by the procedure already outlined, and the findings may then be depicted on a chart (see procedure manual). The load factor indicated on this chart should then be compared with that set forth in the standards.

STAGE IV: DEVELOPING THE TRANSPORTATION PLAN AND FINANCIAL PROGRAM

Now that the Coordinating Committee has fully analyzed the basic transportation and land-use facts, it is in a position to create a realistic transportation plan geared to the needs of the community. The facts which have been collected and studied have revealed the size and nature of the problem. The anticipated number of auto, transit, and truck trips at given future times has been estimated. Deficiencies in the street plant and transit system have been brought into the clear. In the course of arriving at these estimates, the impact of the geographical, historical, social, and economic factors has been weighed.

One thought should be paramount in preparing the transportation plan: It will be effective to the degree that it contributes to the aims of community development. A sound blueprint for overall transportation improvement can be drawn only in light of the fundamental city plan. The two plans must be interwoven and, from a broad point of view, might actually be regarded as one. This fact underscores once again the need for close teamwork between the City Planner, custodian of the city plan, and the other members of the Coordinating Committee in shaping the transportation plan.

Against the background of the city plan and the factual data developed in the various studies, it will soon become apparent that certain general types of solutions seem more practical or promising than others. For example, take the case of a large city which has developed chiefly around public transit. Assume that study has shown that its existing and future traffic difficulties center in and around the downtown area. Assume also that the community plan calls for rehabilitation of this area. In such a case, the logical solution probably would be the development of rapid transit facilities on their own right of way, or coordinated improvement of both transit and highways.

In a community of 200,000 or so, where it is desired to encourage industrial expansion in outlying areas, the solution to the transportation problem undoubtedly will be automotive to a large extent. New circumferential highways will be needed, accompanied perhaps by changes in the transit service to the downtown district.

In some situations, however, the most feasible course will not be quite so obvious. Many of our big cities find it hard to decide how best to service the central business district with transportation. Should rapid transit lines be created? Should there be a balanced program of highway and transit improvements? Or should exclusive attention be given to highway modernization? In the event of such doubts, a careful evaluation of the probable effect of each of the solutions on community development may well be the deciding factor.

As a rule, however, the alternatives will not be too far apart. For example, the choices in a big city may hinge upon the number and location of expressways needed to overcome present and future deficiencies. In a small city, the choice may be between a by-pass and a route through town.

Regardless of whether the alternatives are fairly similar or widely different, a sound decision will be assured if the city has made the recommended studies and properly used the essential facts. The possible solutions can be appraised in terms not only of relative costs, but also of relative benefits, such as safety, comfort, and convenience. The comparative advantages to the community as a whole can be determined. With an adequate supply of facts, such evaluations will no longer be matters of personal opinion or rule of thumb.

The task of the Coordinating Committee during this stage is to develop the alternative plans in sufficient detail to pin down the costs. The financial feasibility of each proposal should be explored. Then the alternatives must be assessed to decide which will best meet the city's transportation requirements and foster the planned goals of community growth. This determination having been made, a report of the Committee's findings should be prepared. It will outline the different plans considered and explain why a particular one is being recommended by the Committee. The report should be presented to the Mayor, the City Council, and the Citizens' Advisory Committee. A copy of the report should also be submitted to the State Highway Department for approval of those portions of the plan in which the Department is concerned.

FORMULATING ALTERNATIVE SOLUTIONS

To simplify the preparation of the alternative solutions, the Coordinating Committee should concentrate on the major capital improvements which each plan will entail in the street and/or transit system. In larger cities, these will involve freeways and rapid transit lines, not arterial street improvements. In communities of 100,000 or so, the capital items will be arterial street betterment, perhaps along with the establishment of a transit lane or street. The chief needs in a small community may be limited to a bridge or two, plus some street widenings and operational changes.

Determination of the major needs will to a large extent reveal the character of the lesser needs, and hence should be considered first.

The kind of major capital improvements involved will more or less define the most likely of the three basic solutions—a predominantly public transit approach; a balanced public transit-automotive approach, and a predominantly automotive approach.

Predominantly Public Transit

A plan oriented toward mass transportation generally centers around an extensive system of transit facilities on their own rights of way, designed mainly to serve the downtown area. This type of plan has been proposed for the City of San Francisco. With the system under consideration in San Francisco, speeds would be comparable to those found on freeways—40 miles per hour—and at the same time transit riding comfort would be considerably enhanced. To supplement these facilities, a limited system of expressways would be needed, chiefly for essential truck and passen-

ger car movement to the downtown area and for automobile traffic in and around suburban areas.

Balanced Transit-Automotive

The balanced approach might call for a transit system on its own right of way, along with a system of expressways for auto movement and express transit service. In addition, an attempt might be made to step up the efficiency of the existing street system by the use of transit lanes or transit streets.

Houston, Texas, has followed such a plan to some degree. There an effort has been made to use the main downtown street as much as possible for moving people. Various traffic control measures in force on the main street are designed to discourage passenger car traffic and facilitate bus transportation. Parallel streets are operated as one-way pairs, thereby encouraging automobiles to use them because of their advantage in travel time over the main street. In addition, these streets are tied in with the freeway system, thus providing quick and easy access to and egress from downtown.

Cleveland, Ohio, in some ways also typifies this concept. Express buses are used on freeways, and a certain number of transit lines have been established on private right of way. The Cleveland transit system has developed 13 miles of rail rapid transit; the suburban community of Shaker Heights operates a rail line that serves downtown Cleveland.

Nashville, Tennessee, has tried to provide equally well for public transit and automobile movement on downtown streets. Transit lanes have been created on several streets to expedite both automobile and bus traffic. (See Figure 11.)

This approach attempts to minimize traffic congestion by encouraging more people to use public transit, especially during rush hours. Provision of faster transit service tends to reduce the demand for expressways and parking facilities.

Predominantly Automotive

Detroit, by and large, is following a predominantly automotive approach. A considerable mileage of expressways has been built and an extensive system is planned. In the design of these controlled access facilities, transit loading and unloading bays are usually included. Transit and passenger car movement are given equal priority, but transit facilities on their own rights of way are not con-

Figure 11   **NASHVILLE BUS LANES**

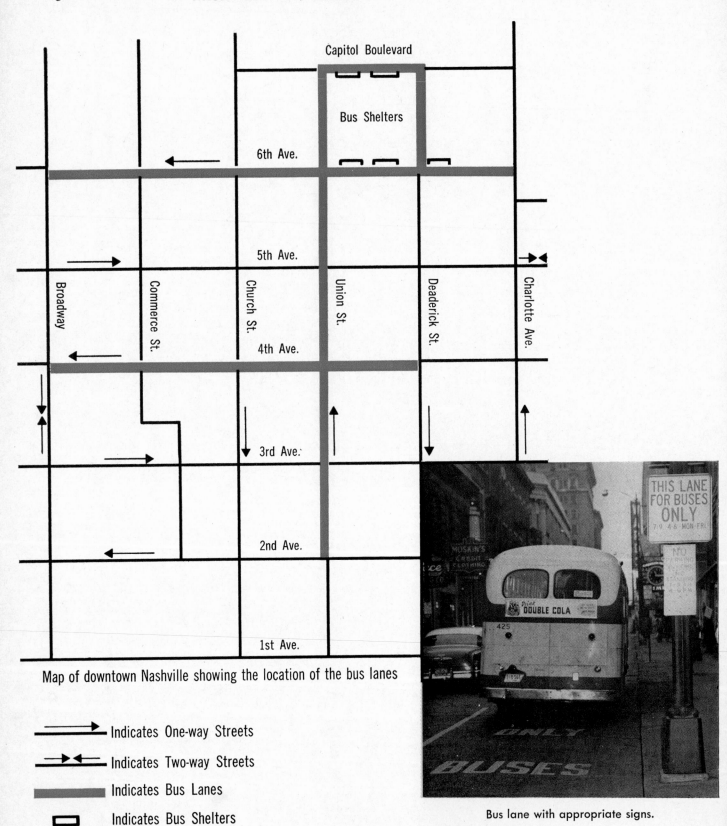

Map of downtown Nashville showing the location of the bus lanes

⟶ Indicates One-way Streets

⟶◄ Indicates Two-way Streets

▬▬ Indicates Bus Lanes

▭ Indicates Bus Shelters

Bus lane with appropriate signs.

Expressways can be used to tie together dispersed residential and industrial areas, which normally are difficult to service by transit. On the other hand, transit can effectively serve areas of concentrated activities like the central business district.

templated because they are not economically justified by the present density of population.

It should be recognized that the particular transportation solution which a community applies will affect land-use patterns to some degree. If a city concentrates on freeway development, the residential pattern will be more widely dispersed than it is in a community depending largely on public transit.

Current research seems to indicate, however, that the population growth outward from the city's center will not vary much, whatever the solution chosen. In other words, increases in population might be fairly comparable under either scheme, but the distribution of population might vary. Logically, the transit plan would draw residences and business enterprises to the vicinity of the

transit lines. In the case of the freeway plan, both residential and industrial developments will tend to group wherever there is highway access.

Delineating Alternative Solutions

In delineating a proposed plan, the Coordinating Committee should try to determine what the essential needs are and how they can be met most effectively. For example, in a small community the basic difficulty may stem from the limited number of crossings over a railroad track. In such a case, the problem is to decide upon the number of additional crossings that will be needed in the future and approximately where they should be located. In another situation, the question may be whether existing streets have sufficient capacity for future traffic. If they do not, the answer may

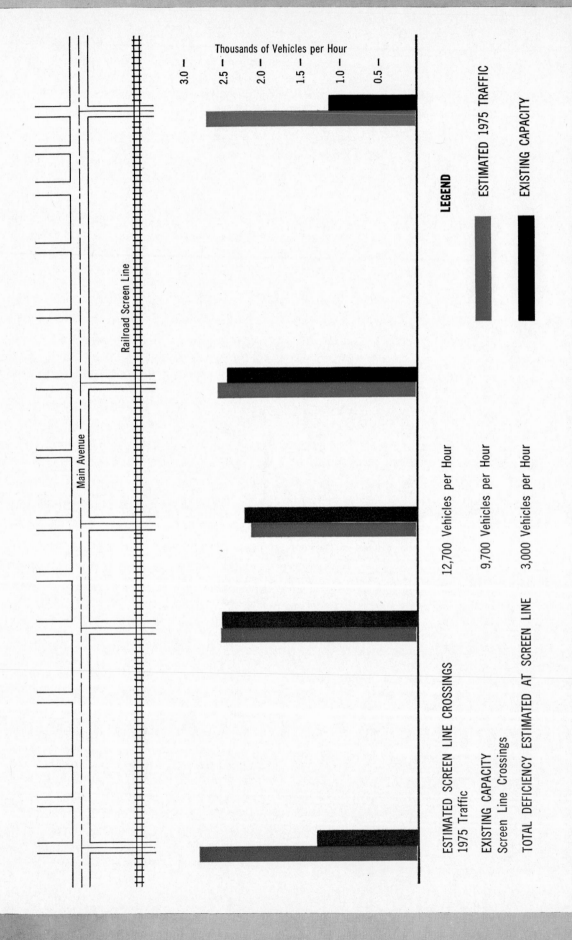

Figure 12

TYPICAL SCREEN LINE CHART

Main Avenue

Railroad Screen Line

Thousands of Vehicles per Hour

3.0
2.5
2.0
1.5
1.0
0.5

LEGEND

ESTIMATED 1975 TRAFFIC

EXISTING CAPACITY

ESTIMATED SCREEN LINE CROSSINGS
1975 Traffic   12,700 Vehicles per Hour

EXISTING CAPACITY
Screen Line Crossings   9,700 Vehicles per Hour

TOTAL DEFICIENCY ESTIMATED AT SCREEN LINE   3,000 Vehicles per Hour be properly located freeways, or expressways with partial access control.

The following technique is suggested for delineating the alternative plans.

In the case of a large urban area, a series of screen lines cutting corridors of traffic should be laid out, together with a cordon line around the central business district—as previously outlined in the traffic studies. For a small community, only one screen line need be used, and the downtown cordon perhaps may be eliminated. Then the street capacity across these lines should be determined and compared with anticipated traffic volumes that will cross them. (The street capacity calculations should reflect the over-all speed standards recommended for the various types of streets. Traffic volume data should be based upon projected O-D data.)

With this comparison it should be possible to determine the number of additional lanes which will be required and the approximate location of such facilities. In other words, such data will help to reveal where improvements are needed and define the type of solution—whether freeway, arterial street, bridge, or by-pass.

To illustrate this procedure, a screen line chart is shown in Figure 12. It depicts existing capacity of the facilities across the screen line and the location of future travel desires across the screen line. It indicates that either two freeway lanes or six lanes of major arterial capacity will be needed across the screen line; it also shows that these deficiencies will occur largely in two areas at the opposite ends of town. Therefore, it becomes quite apparent that the practical solution is two major arterial streets crossing the screen line near the fringe of the community.

For larger communities, more screen lines will be necessary to delineate the plan. A series of screen line charts will reveal what types of street improvements are needed—whether a single facility over the screen line, expansion of the arterial street system, a freeway supplementing the arterial system, or a complete freeway system. With this knowledge and the pattern of traffic derived from the O-D data, it should be possible to outline necessary adjustments or extensions of the street system.

A large city should explore the possibilities of various types of transit operations and the effect they would have on street needs. The screen lines should be evaluated in terms of the number of vehicular trips which would be made across

them if a rapid transit system were provided, or if an express bus operation were installed. In other words, through this procedure it is possible to determine the number of vehicles that will cross the screen line, and the number of people who would take advantage of either the rapid transit or express bus service. This provides the basis for design of an arterial street or freeway system to complement either of these transit alternatives.

Screen lines can be established across corridors of traffic on natural barriers, such as rivers or ravines, or on man-made barriers, such as railroad tracks and parks. If such screen lines are employed, it is easy to determine the capacity over these natural or man-made barriers, since crossings are usually limited. The same procedure may be used by setting up an arbitrary grid of screen lines, say at two-mile intervals throughout the

Figure 13 **THE EFFECT OF STAGGERED WORK HOURS**

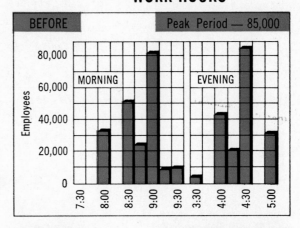

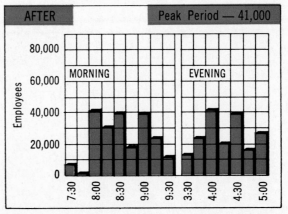

Diagrams show how peak hour movements of federal employees in Washington, D. C., were reduced more than 50 per cent after staggered hour program was initiated. Result was reduced congestion downtown and increased transit efficiency.

metropolitan area. In this case, capacity of the streets crossing these arbitrary lines would be computed and then the travel desires across these lines determined. This method has certain advantages over screen lines established on natural barriers, inasmuch as it may give a more complete picture of needs for freeway routes or arterial streets.

Staggered Work Hours

Before developing preliminary plans, the possibility of staggering work hours and thereby reducing daily peak-hour traffic volumes should be considered. Since design must be related to this rush period, the cost of improvements might be greatly reduced if the peak could be spread out. The potential value of such a scheme for transit operation is illustrated by Figure 13.

At any rate, it is worth while to investigate the feasibility of staggered work hours prior to the development of preliminary plans. The Citizens' Advisory group, with the help of the Coordinating Committee, could make a special study of this project. Since commercial and industrial interests are represented on the Citizens' Committee, they will be in an excellent position to explore the matter. The Committee might also look into the possibilities of staggered hours with reference to large recreational areas and so forth. If it is shown that this approach is practical and necessary, the citizens' group can be a potent factor in obtaining public acceptance.

Developing Preliminary Plans

The next step is to depict on a map the improvements proposed in the alternative plans. The standards that have been adopted, together with the manual of the American Association of State Highway Officials, *A Policy on Arterial Highways in Urban Areas,* the screen line charts, the O-D map, the land-use plan and topographical map are the basic tools that should be used in preparing these preliminary plans.

The standards and the AASHO policy manual will be helpful in guiding the Committee as to over-all transportation objectives, location of facilities, and design criteria. The screen line will indicate the general need for and location of improvements; the O-D map will portray the broad pattern of traffic desiring to cross the screen line and thus indicate the approximate places where new streets are required.

The land-use plan will aid in locating the facilities so that they will fit in with and advance broad community objectives. Conversely, it will help to avoid locations where facilities intrude upon or endanger schools and parks or bisect residential areas.

The review of existing traffic conditions and the knowledge gained of present and future deficiencies make it possible to chart a number of general solutions—each in its own way capable of meeting the transportation needs of the community. As a rule, all such alternative plans will combine street, transit, and terminal improvements, but in varying proportions. Each of the alternative plans should have sufficient flexibility to cope with anticipated developments, both immediate and long range.

As for the transit improvement program, it might include proposed rapid transit facilities; operational improvements such as transit lanes or streets; provisions for operating rail rapid transit or express buses on expressways; and establishment of new routes or adjustment of schedules on existing lines.

Terminal improvements might include needed off-street parking facilities and special truck and transit terminals. It might also involve making better use of present off-street parking spaces, perhaps through a program of ticket validation for shoppers.

All preliminary plans should cover, in addition to transportation facilities which are entirely the responsibility of the city, those that involve other levels of government. Routes to be developed under the Federal Highway Program demand particular attention, since in every case they are construction projects of high priority, designed to bring major benefits to urban areas. Wherever possible, transit and street needs should be coordinated. In areas where both transit and street improvements are required, considerable savings may be made by choosing a right of way which can be used effectively by both.

Here are a few other points that should be kept in mind in preparing the preliminary plan:

It is imperative that, within engineering requirements, proposed major improvements be located so as to cause a minimum of damage to adjacent areas. For example, if the street pattern is basically gridiron in character, it will be very dif-

Progressive communities are combining transportation planning with urban renewal. The plan shown here closely coordinates highway improvements with several redevelopment projects to rejuvenate the central business district.

62

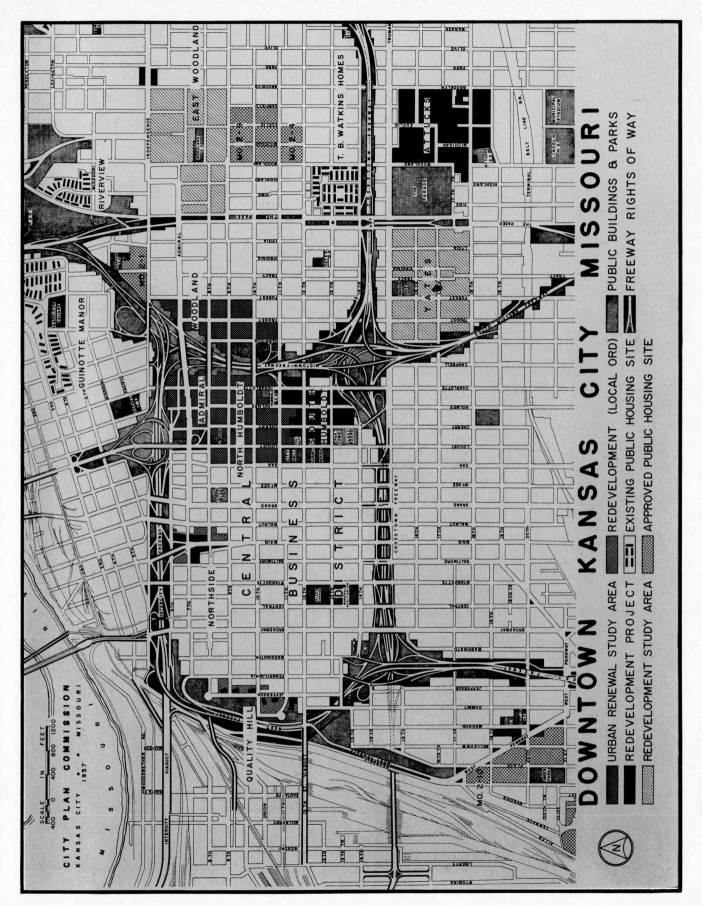

DOWNTOWN KANSAS CITY MISSOURI

CITY PLAN COMMISSION
KANSAS CITY · 1957 · MISSOURI

SCALE IN FEET
400 0 400 800 1200

Legend:
- URBAN RENEWAL STUDY AREA
- REDEVELOPMENT PROJECT
- REDEVELOPMENT STUDY AREA
- REDEVELOPMENT (LOCAL ORD)
- EXISTING PUBLIC HOUSING SITE
- APPROVED PUBLIC HOUSING SITE
- PUBLIC BUILDINGS & PARKS
- FREEWAY RIGHTS OF WAY

ficult and expensive to cut through such a street system at an angle. Such a cut would leave many awkward parcels of land and cause many design problems.

A new transportation facility should avoid a location where it may destroy the established character of the area—such as a fine residential district, for example. Certainly there should be no arbitrary routing of new major facilities through areas where there exists a high degree of productive land use. On the other hand, one of the controlling factors in the choice of route location should be to serve land where high intensity uses are concentrated or anticipated. An illustration of this point would be the development of an expressway through a planned industrial area.

Many cities have land areas outside the central core that lend themselves to the location of new transportation facilities. Improvement of radial streets in the past has stimulated development along them but has often left wedges of unused land between these ribbon developments. Such wedges may offer logical locations for transportation facilities. Many cities have blighted areas slated for rehabilitation. Where these areas tie in with general travel desires, it may be feasible to coordinate transportation improvements with slum clearance and redevelopment programs. In other instances, the location of transportation facilities in blighted areas may stimulate redevelopment.

Often strips of cleared land along natural or man-made barriers (river or lake shore lines, for instance, or near railroad rights of way) may be of sufficient width to accommodate new facilities. Such locations may reduce the conflict with existing transportation facilities and minimize detrimental effects on land development. Locations along the boundaries of parks, golf courses, and private undeveloped tracts of land often will hold down the costs of property damage.

As was shown in Figure 9, the proposed freeway location in Colorado Springs takes advantage of just such opportunities. For example, the north-south freeway has been located adjacent to a railroad and a stream bed. In its course through existing developments it will eliminate a large part of a blighted section on the fringe of the downtown area. On the other freeway location to the west, an old railroad bed has been used for right of way and the route creates no new problems because it follows the edge of a ribbon development along an old arterial street. Of course, all the locational opportunities found in the Colorado Springs plan

will not always present themselves in other communities, but usually there will be sections where new facilities can be routed without involving undue cost, controversy, or inconvenience.

It is suggested that in laying out the freeway pattern or the arterial street pattern every precaution be taken to avoid "merging sections"— i.e., segments of the system which tend to act as an interchange area for two routes. In such cases it is better to cross them and provide the interchange at a single point. As indicated in Figures 15 A and B, if these merging areas are designed into a system, they will cause serious capacity problems.

Testing the Alternative Plans

The soundness of any preliminary plan (or plans) developed by the city will depend entirely upon whether the proposed improvements will be able to handle anticipated traffic in accordance with speed and safety standards. To ascertain this fact, an estimate must be made of the number of vehicles and the transit riders who will use the transportation facilities when fully improved. In doing this, the projection of the origin and destination of personal trips which was made in Stage III should be used. Then, on the basis of the established relations between walking distances, transit speeds, and fares, the number of transit trips by individuals between various zones should be estimated. (These relations will have to be established for each community by analysis of the origin and destination data as outlined in the procedure manual.) The remaining trips, it is assumed, will be made by automobile.

Once the mode of travel is determined for various classes of trips in the urban area, they should be assigned to the appropriate facilities. In the case of public transit movement, trips should be assigned to the rapid transit and bus systems. The auto trips should be assigned to the major arterial streets and expressways. An example, developed by the California Division of Highways, is shown in Figure 14. A procedure manual describes in detail the techniques for proper assignment of trips.

With the total trips allocated to the various systems, it will be fairly apparent whether the proposed design is adequate. These tests may show that certain legs of the systems do not have sufficient capacity to assure desired speed of operation. In such instances it may be necessary to redesign the inadequate sections and apply the

Figure 14

PER CENT OF TRAFFIC DIVERSION
TO EXPRESSWAYS
In Relation to Time and Distance Saved

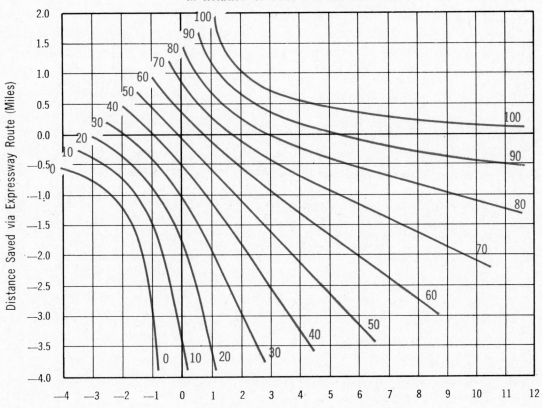

Time Saved via Expressway Route (Minutes)

test again. In other cases the tests may show that certain elements of the proposed system are unnecessary or overdesigned in light of anticipated traffic volumes.

Such a series of tests was made of proposed freeway systems in Cleveland. As shown in Figures 15 A and B, the tests clearly revealed what bottlenecks would develop if either of these two systems were established. By revising the plans it was possible to eliminate the kinks and develop a completely adequate sytem, as shown in Figure 15 C.

Minor Transportation Needs

Once the major proposals have been tested and agreed upon, lesser transportation needs should be determined. These must be met in order to complement the major improvements and remedy structural and operational deficiencies now existing or anticipated. These determinations can be made by comparing the relevant findings in Stage II with the standards in Stage III.

A simple way to group minor transportation requirements is on the basis of (1) physical street needs, (2) traffic engineering measures, and (3) transit improvements.

Physical Street Needs

Under the heading of things to be done to complement the proposed major improvements should be included the elimination of jogs, the realignment of certain arterials, street widenings, intersectional changes, channelizations, and other necessary steps to increase capacity and expedite traffic flow.

On the structural side, it may be necessary to reconstruct certain amounts of street mileage because of poor base, poor drainage, or other structural defects. Some portions of the street system may have to be rebuilt because of their age. Many of these structural needs will be recurring from time to time and must be provided for in any long-term program.

Traffic Engineering Measures

Within the scope of operational improvements would be included traffic routing, traffic

Figure 15   **COMPARATIVE CAPACITY OF
ALTERNATIVE EXPRESSWAY PLANS**

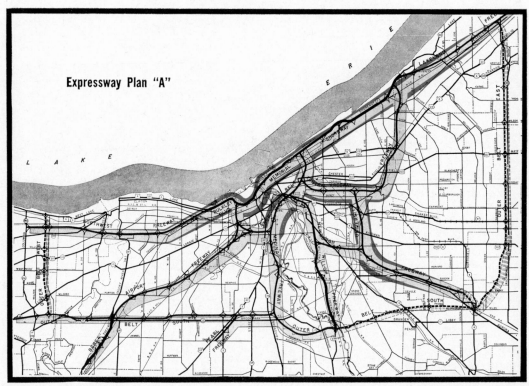

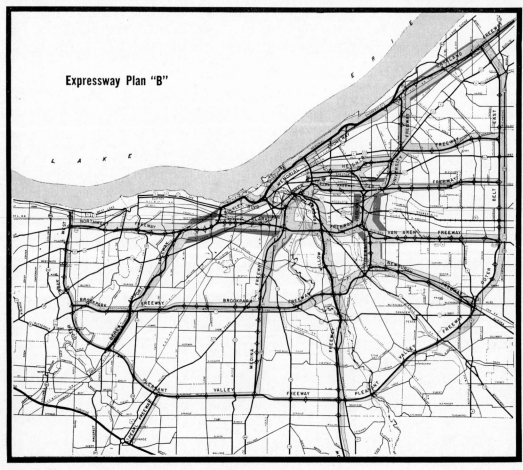

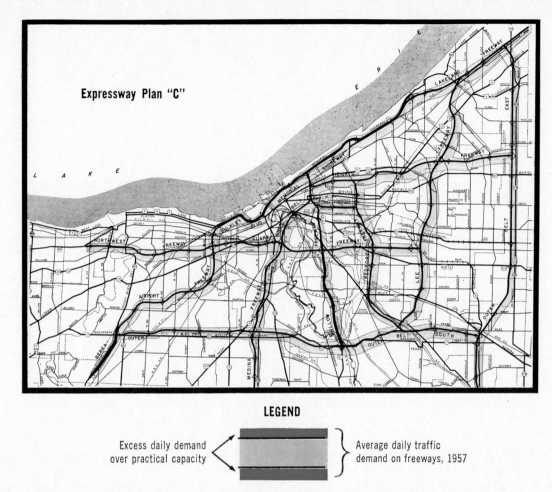

Expressway Plan "C"

LEGEND

Excess daily demand over practical capacity ⟵⟶ ⎫ Average daily traffic demand on freeways, 1957

regulations, and traffic control devices—all utilized to a maximum degree to enable the streets, as classified, to perform their designated functions as efficiently as possible.

Transit Improvements

In an attempt to improve transit service, possible adjustment of routes and schedules should be thoroughly explored. The establishment or extension of express bus routes should be considered. In the crowded downtown area, proper parking and turning controls, as well as better location of bus loading stops, can materially upgrade transit service. The possible need for special transit terminals and loading bays on expressways also should be looked into.

PREPARING THE FINANCIAL PROGRAM

After testing the alternative long-range plans to determine whether they will produce the necessary level of transportation service, the question of financial feasibility remains to be answered. To this end, for each alternative plan a corresponding fiscal program should be prepared.

To develop a financial program, cost estimates are necessary. While it is obvious that preliminary plans cannot be used to produce firm costs, such plans do serve for the making of reasonably accurate estimates.

These cost estimates should include all construction—component parts such as engineering design, land acquisition, land clearance, and maintenance of traffic and transit service during construction. In addition, the costs of providing an adequate maintenance program for both new and old facilities should be computed. Similarly, cost estimates should be made for operations, including the cost of additional personnel and equipment required to meet the expanded program contemplated. The cost of operating transit vehicles should not be considered at this time unless the transit system is publicly owned.

Administrative costs over and above the basic costs of construction, maintenance, and operation should be calculated. These basic cost estimates should be broken down by classification for each proposal, as shown in Table 12.

It might be mentioned in passing that, ac-

67

Table 12
SUMMARY OF BASIC COSTS

	Estimated Cost of Construction	Estimated Cost of Maintenance	Estimated Cost of Operations	Administrative Costs
Expressways				
Major arterials				
Collector streets				
Local streets				
Exclusive transit facilities				
TOTAL				

cording to urban highway needs studies, the costs of arterial streets and expressways over a 20-year period run about 1¢ per vehicle mile. This figure, incidentally, is fairly comparable to the unit cost that has been established for overcoming rural main highway needs in the next 20 years.

After the cost estimates have been made, the scheduling of the various improvements should be undertaken. Since most cities already have a heavy backlog of transportation needs—and these continue to pile up at a tremendous rate, owing to the constant increases in traffic—it is manifestly impossible to meet all the requirements overnight. A realistic catch-up program is the only way out of this dilemma. It is advisable that the community tentatively chart a number of such catch-up programs and, on the basis of feasibility of financing, select the most logical one.

For instance, a city could develop alternative programs for 10-year, 15-year, or 20-year catch-up periods. An example of how alternative programs may be presented graphically is shown in Figure 16.

It is probably superfluous to add that in determining the most appropriate catch-up program, all pertinent aspects of federal and state programs for financing facilities in urban areas should be taken into account.

The next step in developing a financial plan is to review existing revenues related to transportation. In Stage III a projection was made to show sources and amounts of anticipated revenues. The total anticipated revenues should now be compared with the aggregate costs of each of the alternative catch-up programs. This comparison will provide an approximate figure for the additional revenues needed to carry out each program.

Additional Revenue Sources

In exploring possible sources of additional funds, an analysis should be made of the costs of the various elements embraced in the alternative plans, such as expressways, arterials, local streets, transit and terminal facilities. These costs should be compared with the revenues which the elements will produce. If an element will not result in enough revenue to pay for itself, the comparison will show it.

Such disparities should be studied in light of the relative amount of service which the various elements render to the different classes of users, as well as the advantages to specific sections of the community and/or to the community at large. This appraisal should suggest sources which can equitably be called upon to provide the extra revenues needed. If the advantages are communitywide in nature, a general increase in taxes may be necessary. If certain sections of the city are particularly benefited, the answer may be special assessments. If certain users stand to gain most, special user taxes might be levied. In some instances, the additional money may have to be obtained through a combination of these approaches.

To simplify the evaluation of the alternative plans, pertinent data should be organized in a series of tables such as Tables 13, 14, and 15.

As indicated in Table 13, the cost of the several transportation systems should be broken

Figure 16 **ALTERNATIVE CATCH-UP PROGRAMS**

Summary of Estimated Costs

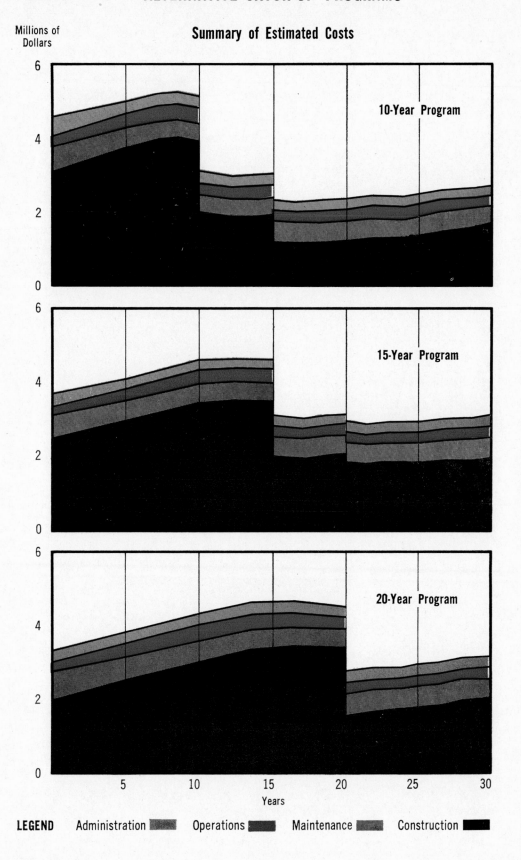

Table 13
ANNUAL COST OF CONSTRUCTING, OPERATING, AND MAINTAINING VARIOUS PORTIONS OF THE TRANSPORTATION SYSTEM

	Downtown	City	Suburban	Total
Expressways	$_____	$_____	$_____	$_____
Major arterial streets	_____	_____	_____	_____
Collector streets	_____	_____	_____	_____
Local streets	_____	_____	_____	_____
Exclusive transit facilities	_____	_____	_____	_____
TOTAL	$_____	$_____	$_____	$_____

Table 14
ANNUAL USER REVENUES DERIVED FROM VARIOUS PORTIONS OF THE TRANSPORTATION SYSTEM

	Downtown	City	Suburban	Total
Expressways	$_____	$_____	$_____	$_____
Major arterial streets	_____	_____	_____	_____
Collector streets	_____	_____	_____	_____
Local streets	_____	_____	_____	_____
Exclusive transit facilities	_____	_____	_____	_____
TOTAL	$_____	$_____	$_____	$_____

down for various sections of the urban area. Cost figures should include construction, maintenance, operation, and overhead expenses related to the several systems.

User revenues associated with the various transportation systems also should be broken down by sections (Table 14). The revenues which are assigned to each system should include all user taxes, as well as tolls and fares.

For analysis of system use, a table similar to 15 should be developed to show mode of travel and purpose of trips during peak and off-peak hours on the several systems in different sections of the city. To depict all trips on a comparable basis, they should be presented in terms of vehicle miles.

When deliberating the fiscal aspects, it is well to review the ways in which all public improve-

70

Table 15
USE OF TRANSPORTATION SYSTEMS
Relation between Vehicle Trip Purpose, Time of Travel,
Destination of Travel
(All trips in vehicle miles)

ROAD SYSTEM AND TRIP PURPOSE	Place			Time	
	Downtown	City	Suburban	Peak	Off-Peak
EXPRESSWAYS					
Automobile					
Work	_____	_____	_____	_____	_____
Business	_____	_____	_____	_____	_____
Other	_____	_____	_____	_____	_____
Truck	_____	_____	_____	_____	_____
Transit	_____	_____	_____	_____	_____
MAJOR ARTERIALS					
Automobile					
Work	_____	_____	_____	_____	_____
Business	_____	_____	_____	_____	_____
Other	_____	_____	_____	_____	_____
Truck	_____	_____	_____	_____	_____
Transit	_____	_____	_____	_____	_____
COLLECTOR STREETS					
Automobile					
Work	_____	_____	_____	_____	_____
Business	_____	_____	_____	_____	_____
Other	_____	_____	_____	_____	_____
Truck	_____	_____	_____	_____	_____
Transit	_____	_____	_____	_____	_____
LOCAL STREETS					
Automobile					
Work	_____	_____	_____	_____	_____
Business	_____	_____	_____	_____	_____
Other	_____	_____	_____	_____	_____
Truck	_____	_____	_____	_____	_____
Transit	_____	_____	_____	_____	_____
EXCLUSIVE TRANSIT FACILITIES	_____	_____	_____	_____	_____

ments are financed. By and large, there are four principal methods:

1. Current revenues (including taxes and other revenues shared)
2. Borrowing (government obligations and revenue bonds)
3. Special assessments
4. Grants-in-aid and other contributions (state and federal)

The extent to which any of these methods can be used depends upon a number of factors, including but not limited to the following:

1. The size and nature of improvement programs undertaken
2. The fiscal policy of the governing body and the desires of its constituent public
3. Revenue sources, revenue restrictions, and debt limitations
4. The size and nature of projects eligible for state and federal grants-in-aid

In seeking additional revenue sources to finance the long-range program it is vital to keep other urban requirements fully in mind. Needs for other types of public works also have increased at a phenomenal rate, along with rapid population growth and urbanization. Hence it is unwise to contemplate tapping revenue sources which must provide for these other municipal needs.

EVALUATION OF PROPOSALS

Having established what the alternative plans would cost and how they might be financed, the next job is to appraise the relative merits of the plans. Such an evaluation should seek to determine, on the one hand, which proposal offers the most benefits to users and to the community as a whole and, on the other, which is most practicable.

The accepted yardsticks for measuring benefits to the user are savings in travel time and oper-

ating costs. A procedure manual explains how these savings should be calculated. The findings related to each alternative plan may then be summarized in table form.

With regard to impact on the community, judgment evaluations of benefits as well as of potential drawbacks should be made. These will involve such important considerations as:

Will the plan help or hinder downtown revival?

Will it help to break the traffic jam?

Will it encourage industrial expansion? Increase property values?

What will be the effect on built-up residential areas? On development of outlying areas?

Will urban decentralization be retarded more by one plan than another?

Will the community profit more from a bypass or from a route through town?

Will it be better in the long run to move people by transit than by individual transportation?

The plans should also be judged on the basis of which best meets the test of practicability. Whether or not the financial program for the plan is entirely realistic is a matter deserving of close scrutiny. The degree to which the plan fits in with geographical, economic, social, and historical factors should be considered. Special administrative or legal problems entailed in the plan should be fully weighed.

On the basis of all the facts which the Coordinating Committee has been able to bring to bear upon this subject—community and user benefits, practicability, and costs—a decision can now be reached as to the most promising of the alternative plans. The plans, along with their pros and cons, should be fully elucidated in a final report. The report of course should give all the pertinent reasons why the Committee selected a particular plan as most feasible and most advantageous to the community.

STAGE V: ADOPTING THE PREFERRED PLAN AND FINANCIAL PROGRAM

Every step described and recommended thus far in this Guide has been directed toward a single goal: the development of a factual, orderly, and continuous plan of transportation improvement designed to gain legislative approval and the necessary funds to carry it out.

In any community, the legislative body or Council is, in effect, a board of directors chosen by the voters to set policy and make decisions on matters affecting the common welfare. In adopting a transportation plan, as in other major decisions, the city's lawmakers must reflect the majority opinion of the citizens. It is of vital importance, therefore, that the citizens understand the issues— that public opinion be *informed* opinion. For the legislative decision to be made in this case may have a profound effect not only on transportation service—but also on the physical, economic, and social character of the community—for many years to come.

While it is true that even a well-informed public sometimes turns down a worth while program, more often than not failure to win public acceptance stems from lack of information— which always generates doubts and misconceptions to fill the void. Given the facts, citizens have a basis for intelligent support, particularly when the facts plainly indicate that a proposed course will bring substantial benefits to themselves and their communities.

These facts emphasize the need for a large-scale program of public information, utilizing every possible medium, to explain the recommended transportation plan to the people. Even more necessary is strong civic leadership to sponsor and direct the information program, and to serve as the nucleus for mobilizing public support.

If the Citizens' Advisory Committee in the community has been properly organized, it will embrace the required leadership within its membership. With top executives of business, industry, labor, service and professional groups, broadcasting, advertising, and the press represented, the Advisory Committee contains influential people who not only are in themselves the best possible ambassadors for the transportation program, but who through their organizations can help supply the informational skills and facilities for the big job of public education involved.

PUBLIC INFORMATION ASPECTS

If the Advisory Committee has been working closely with the Technical Coordinating Committee from the start, the citizen leaders will have been fully apprised of all the significant developments and findings culminating in the report on the alternative improvement plans. When the report is completed, the Coordinating Committee should carefully brief the members of the citizens' group on the various alternatives and explain in detail why the plan being recommended seems best for the community.

With this background, and on the basis of the facts developed, it is probable that the advisory group will concur fully with the conclusions of the technicians of the Coordinating Committee. If any points of disagreement on the plans should arise between the two groups, every effort should be made to resolve or adjust them before embarking on the public education campaign.

It is imperative to have a united front with respect to the recommended plan; otherwise, the two committees may eventually be working at cross-purposes, the public may become confused and disconcerted, and the whole transportation program may be endangered.

In most cases it would be advisable to center responsibility for the public education program in the Citizens' Committee, designating it as the clearinghouse for all informational activities. Committee members whose companies or organizations employ public relations experts can contribute greatly to the success of the campaign by making their services available to direct the work.

As has been said, all the principal media of mass communication should be utilized, including newspapers and other publications, radio and television, meetings, speakers' bureaus, and displays, among others. The big challenge is proper preparation of materials, tailored to the special requirements of the different media—whether news releases for the press, scripts for radio, speeches for speakers, or other. Here is where the help of the professionals is invaluable, and the degree of such assistance may have a material effect on results.

By and large, the first essential in communicating a complex transportation plan to the gen-

Newspapers and Other Printed Matter

The press, in most communities, will prove to be the backbone of the public information effort. Therefore it is important that management of local newspapers be represented on the Advisory Committee. The press should be kept abreast of developments in every stage of the transportation program. When the recommended program takes shape, some newspapers will recognize the public-service values in running a series of articles on the salient features of the plan, how it was developed, and what it would mean to the community.

Of course, all newspapers in a city may not be equally receptive to the proposed plan, but if the facts have been adequately developed and the plan soundly prepared in the manner outlined in

PRESS

RADIO

T V

MAGAZINES HOUSE ORGANS

POSTERS

PUBLIC SPEAKERS

All media of mass communication should be enlisted to inform the public about the recommended transportation plan. Responsibility for the public education program should center in the Citizens' Advisory Committee.

eral public is to simplify and "humanize" the subject. Data must be presented in a form that can be comprehended quickly and easily. At the same time, every fact offered must be accurate and capable of documentation.

Wherever possible, the story should be told in terms of human interests and aspirations. The strongest appeal lies in the benefits and advantages that will accrue from the recommended plan—the savings in life and limb, the reduction of daily travel time, the savings in gasoline and the wear and tear on the family car, the added comfort and convenience, the enhancement of property values, the stimulation of economic activity.

this Guide, the opportunity for unjustified criticism will be minimized.

Pamphlets, brochures, magazine articles, and newsletters are some of the other printed media that can be used in reaching large numbers of people. In more than one city, a public-spirited commercial establishment, bank, or industrial concern has published an illustrated digest of a transportation plan, for distribution among employees, customers, and the general public.

Radio and Television

Like the press, local broadcasters should be brought into the transportation planning program

74

at the time it is first organized in Stage I. Radio interviews with the various municipal department heads represented on the Coordinating Committee, panel discussions, instructive talks by technicians and civic leaders can all help to disseminate the essentials of the plan and keep public attention focused upon it. Television, in some respects, is even more adaptable for the informational job, since visual aids such as charts, maps, displays, and models can be used.

Presentations at Meetings

Informal meetings arranged by the Citizens' Advisory Committee and special presentations before civic and service groups are other effective methods of creating informed public opinion and a favorable climate for the transportation improvement plan.

The informal meetings can be scheduled in schools and other available public buildings, and conducted in "town hall" style, with an Advisory Committee member presiding and Coordinating Committee people on hand to explain technical aspects and answer questions from the floor. Many business, labor, fraternal, civic, and religious organizations will welcome an interesting presentation on the transportation and traffic plans of the city, and special teams drawn from both the Citizens' and Coordinating Committees can be formed to service requests for such appearances.

Graphic materials, like large charts and maps to highlight or summarize basic information, can be developed and used equally well for different types of meetings. It goes without saying that the Committee people entrusted with the presentations should be fully conversant with all elements of the proposed plan, including its factual basis, the nature of the improvements needed, their general location, the costs and anticipated benefits, the metropolitan aspects of the program, and so forth. For this purpose, it will be extremely useful to prepare a speaker's manual or a kit of basic materials, both for advance preparation and for ready reference.

Since the presentation teams undoubtedly will be called upon to answer queries that go beyond the physical details of the plan, the basic materials kit should enable them to make intelligent reply to many such questions as these:

1. How is property for right of way to be acquired and how will the property owner be compensated?

2. How are the displaced residents and business establishments to be relocated?

3. Will taxes be increased? If so, how much, and in what areas?

4. If a plan is approved, will its cost prevent construction of other needed improvements, such as parks, playgrounds, schools, and fire stations?

5. What is the land acquisition and construction schedule to be followed?

Members of the legislative body will find it to their advantage to attend some of the meetings. The Councilmen will have the opportunity thereby to hear at first hand the questions raised, the degree of interest and public support in evidence, and the nature of any opposition to the recommended plan.

Following this intensive educational effort, the Advisory Committee should make a digest of responsible suggestions offered by the public at the various meetings and present them for the consideration of the Coordinating Committee.

LEGISLATIVE ACTION

When the City Council takes up the transportation improvement plan, it will schedule formal hearings on the proposals. At the first session, the spokesman for the Coordinating Committee will highlight the main features of the recommended plan, indicating such modifications as may have been made in light of public opinion expressed at the informal meetings. The chairman and perhaps other members of the Citizens' Advisory Committee should attend to give their endorsement of the plan.

In smaller communities the hearings probably will be limited to one or two sessions. The amount of time allotted in any community will depend upon state requirements, the public interest generated, and the number of people desiring to be heard. It is important to give all citizens an opportunity to be heard, even though some of the arguments for or against may appear irrelevant or unnecessary.

Of course, in cases where improvements proposed in the plan involve federal-aid highways entering, traversing, or by-passing the community, the state will hold hearings on these particular facilities, as prescribed in the 1956 Highway Act.

After the formal hearings are concluded, the Council may wish to confer further with the technical staff to clarify certain aspects of the plan, including cost estimates, locations, possible methods of financing, and so forth. These conferences may result in further adjustments. In all probability, too, before the plan is made final the Council will want to consult with state and county highway officials on those parts which specifically concern them.

When and if the Council ultimately approves the plan, the action carries the implicit intention of providing funds to finance the recommended improvements. It goes without saying that in making this commitment, the legislative body has given full consideration to the financial requirements, and the possible sources of revenue for other necessary improvements such as schools, police and fire protection, recreational facilities, libraries, and other components of a well-rounded public works program.

The point to be stressed is that approval of the transportation plan should be accompanied by an adequate revenue program.

The financial program obviously may take different forms in different communities, depending mainly upon the sources of revenue to be used. Some cities will rely on bond issues to pay for the major improvements; some will prefer to rely on current income—making them "pay as you go."

These approaches in every case will require state enabling legislation. A special referendum or a charter amendment may be necessary. Whatever is required should be done as quickly as possible after the plan is approved, while it is still fresh in the minds of the public.

STAGE VI: CARRYING OUT THE PLAN

With the City Council's approval of the plan and adoption of a financial program, the Coordinating Committee can proceed to execute the improvements. This will be a many-faceted job, loaded with knotty problems. It will involve a great deal of creative effort, tact, and resolution. Above all, it will require a high degree of teamwork.

The technicians at the helm of the improvement program will have to take account of such difficult matters as the proper dovetailing of city-county-state programs; acquisition of right of way; moving of displaced families and commercial establishments; clearing and grading of land; provision of detours; coordination of the work of the various contractors to be employed; and getting users accustomed to the new facilities. Much attention also will have to be given to public comfort and convenience during this developmental stage.

Priorities for the numerous projects will have to be established so that the most important facilities from the standpoint of community benefits will be built first. In addition, the improvement plan and financial program will have to be kept up to date by continuing the fact-gathering operation described in Stage II.

In connection with these large-scale activities, it is essential that the Coordinating Committee prepare, each year, a report noting significant changes in the transportation picture and setting forth project priorities in light of these changes. The report likewise will inform the City Council about scheduled projects and the work that should be undertaken during the coming year. It also will give the Citizens' Advisory Committee a chance to review the program every year, and thus insure its support for annual allocation of funds for transportation projects.

The report, moreover, provides a basis of intergovernmental coordination, since it outlines for the county and state highway agencies and for the various city department heads the work to be done during each ensuing year, thereby encouraging closer integration of activities in which the several parties have a mutual interest.

ESTABLISHING TRANSPORTATION PRIORITIES

A first-things-first approach in meeting the community's transportation needs is effected through use of a priorities scheme. Priority needs in a city are usually limited to what are called "capital improvements," which do not include maintenance and similar recurring items. (How to differentiate between maintenance and capital improvement projects is fully explained in the procedure manual on Accounting.)

The establishment of an order of relative importance, which is valid from a variety of standpoints, is the main object of a priority rating scheme. The criteria include such factors as community interest, availability of funds, limitations on revenue procurement, state highway programs and programs of neighboring jurisdictions, other public works programs within the city, cost, and benefits.

The Coordinating Committee should adopt a procedure which assures a systematic review of these factors in connection with each individual project. This is the purpose of the project Priority Rating Sheet shown in Figure 17, which groups the significant factors into two categories.

The first—community benefits—is the broader since it is, in effect, the measure of the project's value to the city as a whole. Under this category, according to the procedure manual, assessment would be made of (1) its importance to the community and (2) its contribution to sound community development.

The second category covers cost-benefit analysis of the proposed projects. This analysis should

Figure 17

PRIORITY RATING SHEET

Project No._____ Description:_____

District:_____ State Highway Classification:_____

Traffic Volumes   Now:_____ 20 Years:_____

CLASSIFICATION   COST ESTIMATE (Date)

Street: Expressway   ☐   R.O.W.   _____

         Major Arterial ☐   Grading   _____

         Collector   ☐   Structures _____

         Local   ☐   Surface   _____

Transit: Express   ☐   Other   _____

         Local   ☐   TOTAL _____

	Now	0-5 Yrs.	5-10 Yrs.	10-15 Yrs.	15-20 Yrs.
TIME PROJECT NEEDED	☐	☐	☐	☐	☐

PRIORITY FACTORS   Rating

Community Benefits   _____ _____ _____ _____ _____

Cost Benefits Analysis   _____ _____ _____ _____ _____

TOTAL RATING   _____ _____ _____ _____ _____

PROGRAM REQUIREMENTS_____

_____

ADJUSTED PRIORITY

Rating   _____ _____ _____ _____ _____

Program Period_____ _____ _____ _____ _____

WORK SCHEDULE   (Year)

R.O.W.   _____   **Note:** Does this scheduling date
                               require that some stop gap
Grading   _____   measure be taken_____? If so,
                               prepare a project form and
Structure   _____   determine priority rating.

Surface   _____

Other   _____

Completion   _____

include an evaluation of the benefits to the users in terms of time saving and accident reduction. In addition, the urgency of replacing or reconstructing various transportation facilities should be demonstrated on the basis of economy and user safety and convenience factors.

It is recommended that these criteria be employed for every project in order to arrive at its appropriate rating. The projects ranking highest will of course merit first attention.

After this scheme or a similar one has been applied, projects with the highest ratings should be reviewed from the standpoint of their fitting into an efficient sequence of construction. In line with this consideration, a final appraisal of project priorities should then be made.

As an illustration, in building a freeway it might be necessary to widen an arterial into which it will feed. In this event, it would be logical to widen the street at the same time the freeway leg is under construction.

As is well known, the public generally does not look with favor upon an overconcentration of projects in one area of the city, even though all may be of the utmost importance. Consequently, it is suggested that the city be divided into several districts, with the projects within each district rated as to their priority.

The above procedure is only one of several schemes that might be used to establish priorities. Which procedure is selected will depend upon local conditions, but in any event it should be designed to indicate clearly to the public that the priority decisions were based not on whims, but on facts.

Capital Improvement Program

When the project priorities have been set, an effort should be made to coordinate them with other capital improvement projects in the community. Coordination is normally achieved through the Capital Improvement Program. This, usually covering a six-year period, specifies when the various capital improvements will be undertaken.

Responsibility for developing the Capital Improvement Program generally rests with either the City Planning Commission or the Chief Administrative Officer, though it is actually prepared as a cooperative effort with other municipal agencies. Since the representatives of the Planning Commission and the Chief Administrative Officer are active on the Coordinating Committee, it should not

be difficult to correlate transportation needs with other city requirements in the Capital Improvement Program.

As has already been indicated, project priorities should be reviewed annually on the basis of changing conditions. Therefore, the Coordinating Committee should reappraise the transportation needs every year, and where necessary suggest changes in the Capital Improvement Program.

COORDINATING THE WORK PROGRAM

Another important function of the Coordinating Committee is to insure proper integration of the work program. This calls for review and revision of detailed engineering plans, scheduling of work projects, and establishment of detours during construction periods.

The engineering plans for high priority projects should be completed at least a year in advance of the time that work is scheduled to get under way. In the case of projects which are the responsibility of the city, the plans normally would be prepared by the City Engineer's office or the Department of Public Works, but in some instances by the Traffic Engineering Division or the transit agency. On the other hand, plans or engineering drawings for federal-aid or state-assistance projects are usually prepared by the State Highway Department.

An early review of the plans will tend to foster harmonious relations between the several city departments concerned, the county, and the State Highway Department in carrying out the necessary improvements. It also will improve coordination of the work to be done by the different agencies involved.

Because of the obsolete laws that govern land acquisition in many states, it is doubly important that sufficient time be allowed for this purpose in preparing the work schedule. For projects which will involve displacement of persons and business establishments, careful thought should be given to the problem of relocation. Failure to plan for relocation in advance may result in unfavorable public relations and delay the program.

The schedule should also take account of special measures and traffic adjustments which will be necessary during the construction period. Some projects will require temporary roadways and transit service, special pedestrian walks, signs, safety fencing, barricades, lighting, temporary signals, and so forth. Before detours are established, the police should be consulted and the public informed. At all times the public's safety, comfort, and convenience should be paramount.

KEEPING THE PLAN UP TO DATE

Since urban transportation is dynamic, no plan can be considered final. Hence it is essential to continue collecting basic transportation data for use in reevaluating the improvement plan in light of changing conditions.

One of the most effective ways of determining where a plan needs adjustment is to keep a continuous record of traffic volumes across the screen lines used in developing the plan. These volume trends should then be compared with the traffic projected across the screen lines on the basis of the O-D data.

If there is considerable disparity between them, the variances should be looked into. They may be due to unexpected land development, such as new industrial areas or a new shopping center. Whether this or something else is the reason, the land-use plan should be reviewed—at least those sections where existing development patterns seem to be out of key with the plan. The review may call for changes in the transportation plan in certain parts of the community. Such modifications should be developed in accordance with the techniques outlined in Stage IV.

In most cases, these adjustments will not substantially affect the cost of the over-all improvement plan, but if they do, the financial program should be reappraised.

The maintenance and operational programs, too, must be kept up to date in accordance with any new information developed. Accumulated cost data on maintenance will undoubtedly help to improve maintenance programs. For example, analysis of these maintenance costs makes it possible to find out whether the community is spending too little or too much on maintenance. It also will indicate whether it is better to reconstruct a street than to maintain it.

The longer this information is gathered, the more valuable it will become in shaping the maintenance program. An ample backlog of facts also will make it easier to establish correlation between such items as pavement type and road life—essen-tial in developing a program of street reconstruction. Similar correlations can be developed for other maintenance activities, such as vehicle and equipment maintenance, street cleaning, snow removal, pavement marking, and street lighting.

In the field of traffic operations, the Traffic Engineer should keep constant tabs on changes in traffic speed, vehicular volumes, and accidents. He should constantly compare these items with the adopted standards and past trends. By keeping abreast of the trends, he will be in a better position to improve the safety and efficiency of the street system.

For example, he may find that vehicular movement on a street is slowing down each year. By comparing observed speeds with the standards, he will know when he should recommend the removal of curb parking. Thereafter, continued studies of traffic service will reveal whatever impact this measure is having on travel speeds and accidents.

As has been stated, a continuous data-collecting program is more or less standard operating procedure with most transit companies. The uses of such information are manifold.

The data, for instance, may reveal a falling-off of bus speed on a certain route. Joint investigation by the Transit Manager and the Traffic Engineer may suggest an adjustment of signal timing as the solution. In another case, changes observed in load factors may point to the need for increasing or decreasing bus headways. Again, the facts on a certain line may show the advisability of revising the schedule to accommodate a new demand for service.

In these and many other ways, the factual program repeatedly demonstrates its value in maintaining efficiency and an adequate level of service in transit operations.

To sum up, the transportation plan must, above all, be a *living* plan—definite and firm as to ultimate objectives yet flexible enough to be adaptable to changing conditions. That is why the factual foundation upon which a sound improvement program is predicated must be constantly replenished and strengthened. Properly used, the facts will continue to be guideposts toward increasingly better transportation in the American community.

IMPROVING TRANSPORTATION ADMINISTRATION

Whether or not it is so recognized by the community, the management of local transportation has become a major job—one of the most vital in the whole field of public administration.

It is a complex task requiring close technical coordination. A smooth-working organization is indispensable to carry out the interrelated functions of planning, constructing, operating, and maintaining the system. Without such an organization, officials are severely handicapped, sometimes to a point where they are even unable to take advantage of technical know-how available within the city government.

In most cities the existing administrative structure is a relic of pre-automobile days. As a rule it evolved haphazardly. Few people foresaw the incredible growth of motor transportation and the welter of problems it would bring in its wake. As these problems increased, cities tried to solve them with expedients. Responsibilities were parceled out, sometimes foisted upon existing agencies, sometimes delegated to newly created ones. Such diffusion naturally results in divided authority, duplicated effort, conflicts, and waste—so that often even relatively minor projects are retarded by costly and unnecessary delays.

In the case of the older municipal services, such as water supply, welfare, and recreation, unity of the managerial structure and centralized authority are provided for in the city charter. Few cities have given charter recognition to street and traffic administration as a first-line municipal activity of incalculable importance in the daily life of the community.

Belatedly, cities are coming to recognize that the size and far-reaching impact of urban traffic problems demand the closest possible correlation of the basic functions. They are, in effect, the gears of the administrative machine producing street transportation, and to the degree that they fail to

mesh properly, the service and safety of the public are jeopardized.

Conducting an Administrative Study

To correct the widespread diffusion of responsibilities and duties that exists in this field, many cities sooner or later will have to revamp their organizational structure. Consequently, as part of the transportation planning program outlined in this Guide, it would be highly advantageous to make an administrative study.

Highway work schedules should be timed to fit in with other city activities such as utilities improvements, housing developments, and school construction. At the same time, necessary disruption of traffic should be held to a minimum.

At what particular point in the program such a study should be done will depend upon local conditions. In cases where cities have made administrative adjustments or have conducted an appraisal of street and traffic management fairly recently, it is probably not necessary to carry out

Figure 18

STREAMLINING TRANSPORTATION MANAGEMENT

A typical approach toward functional consolidation.

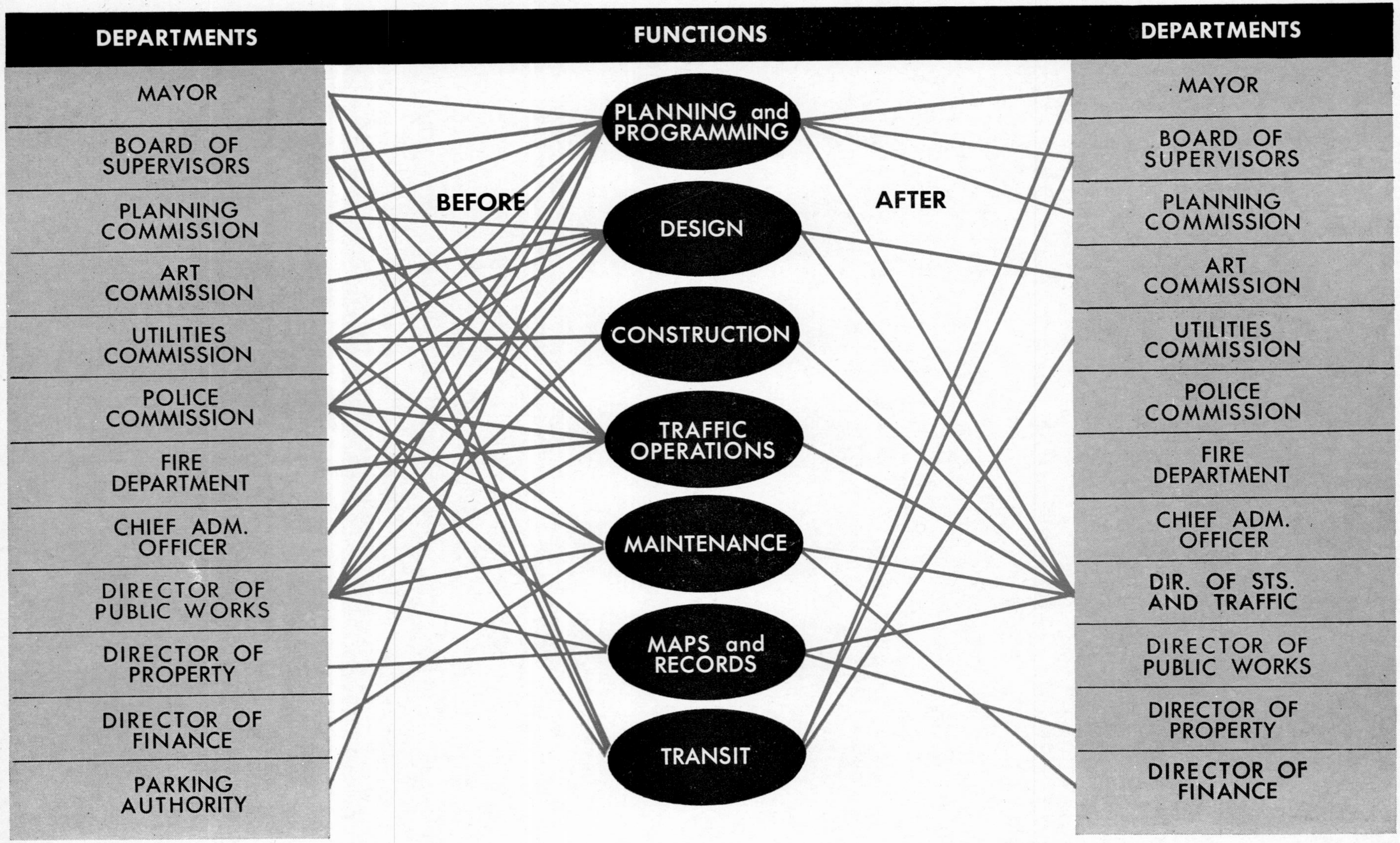

DEPARTMENTS

MAYOR

BOARD OF SUPERVISORS

PLANNING COMMISSION

ART COMMISSION

UTILITIES COMMISSION

POLICE COMMISSION

FIRE DEPARTMENT

CHIEF ADM. OFFICER

DIR. OF STS. AND TRAFFIC

DIRECTOR OF PUBLIC WORKS

DIRECTOR OF PROPERTY

DIRECTOR OF FINANCE

FUNCTIONS

AFTER

PLANNING and PROGRAMMING

DESIGN

CONSTRUCTION

TRAFFIC OPERATIONS

MAINTENANCE

MAPS and RECORDS

TRANSIT

BEFORE

DEPARTMENTS

MAYOR

BOARD OF SUPERVISORS

PLANNING COMMISSION

ART COMMISSION

UTILITIES COMMISSION

POLICE COMMISSION

FIRE DEPARTMENT

CHIEF ADM. OFFICER

DIRECTOR OF PUBLIC WORKS

DIRECTOR OF PROPERTY

DIRECTOR OF FINANCE

PARKING AUTHORITY

a study in the early stages of the transportation planning program. In fact, it may be best to wait until all stages have been completed and thereby profit from the information developed and the experience gained. Both may point up the need for further administrative revamping.

However, if the community has made few or no changes in the management setup in recent years, an administrative study should be launched during the early stages of the transportation planning program.

Since the administrative organization responsible for transportation includes various members of the Coordinating Committee, it would be advisable that the administrative study be assigned to someone outside the Committee. A logical choice for this task would be the Chief Administrator or his assistant. From his vantage point, this executive can see problems in their proper perspective —problems of personnel, of inter- and intra-departmental relations, of coordination of transportation activities among different jurisdictions. A procedure manual describes in detail how such a study should be approached, what basic information is needed, and how it should be analyzed.

The person named to direct the administrative study should consult closely with the department heads represented on the Technical Coordinating Committee. Together they should review the various transportation functions being performed—who is legally responsible for carrying them out, what specific activities are involved, what personnel are used, and what the relations are between various departments and agencies involved in this field.

An administrative survey of this type will help the Chief Administrative Officer and the respective department heads in the following ways:

1. It will serve to identify weaknesses in structural organization and functional coordination.

2. It will help to put the transportation management job into proper perspective in terms of the work program involved, personnel, costs, skills, training, and necessary teamwork.

3. It will supply facts useful in making an objective evaluation and classification of problems according to their nature and urgency.

4. It will provide the basic information necessary for intelligent action to improve transportation management.

TRANSPORTATION FUNCTIONS

In carrying out an administrative study, it must be recognized that the basic transportation functions are much broader than the transportation planning and programing functions outlined in this Guide. Besides planning and programing, they include design and construction, operations, and maintenance, as well as all routine administrative activities.

Transportation Planning and Programing

Transportation planning, as has already been indicated, is the tool for scientifically determining traffic and transit needs and the most practical ways to meet them. It is a staff function that serves to correlate all the broad elements of design and construction, maintenance and operations.

The stock in trade of planning and programing are the classes of facts developed in the studies outlined in Stage II. The minimum basic responsibilities in these two activities are:

1. Conducting studies of traffic volume, peak loads, origin and destination of trips, parking, speed and delay, street classification and capacity, and research in related fields.

2. Determining present and future needs for streets, street lighting, parking, transit facilities, and terminal facilities, and establishing priorities for such facilities.

3. Participating in the preparation of a master transportation plan. Such a plan should relate transit and auto transportation to each other and to over-all city development. This includes all plans involving transit, street, and terminal improvements.

4. Coordinating transportation improvement programs with other municipal activities.

5. Developing financial plans so that the improvement program can be carried out.

Design and Construction

The design and construction function includes such activities as the determination of the type of physical improvements required and the preparation of detailed engineering plans, as well as the supervision of the construction of the improvements. This function of course covers both relatively minor projects like channelizing an intersection and major construction jobs like a freeway. The activities involved are precisely those necessary to carry out whatever transportation improvement program has been adopted by the community (Stage VI).

Broadly speaking, the major duties involved in this function are to:

1. Establish standards for the design and construction of all transportation facilities.

2. Conduct surveys to determine line, grade, and elevations.

3. Prepare detailed engineering drawings and specifications of all new street, transit, and terminal improvements.

4. Inspect the construction of all improvements and review all contracts for transportation improvements.

Operations

The general task of transportation operations is making sure that the total available system is used to best advantage. This means efficiency in the movement of people and goods and maximum safety, comfort, and convenience to all users.

This function covers a wide range of activities such as determining need for traffic control devices and the most appropriate types, the installation of the devices, and operation of the transit system. The list of the principal responsibilities includes:

1. Determination of the location, type, and specifications of traffic control devices.

2. Determination of necessary controls on curb parking, standing, and stopping.

3. Installation and timing of traffic signals.

4. Establishment of turning controls, parking regulations, speed controls, one-way streets, through streets, stop intersections, and any other measures deemed necessary.

5. Development of transit routes, schedules, and service improvements.

Maintenance

The primary purpose of maintenance is to keep the physical plant in good operating condition. A second important objective is to protect the large public investment in transportation facilities.

The entire transportation program is influenced by the degree of efficiency of maintenance work. Unless this function is competently carried out, excessive maintenance costs will cut heavily into funds needed for new street improvements. The primary maintenance duties are to:

1. Maintain and repair all transportation facilities and structures.

2. Maintain all transportation equipment, including transit vehicle and street maintenance machinery.

3. Install and maintain uniform signs, pavement markings, parking meters, street lights, and traffic signals.

4. Perform street cleaning, including snow removal and so forth.

The procedure manual discusses the transportation functions in greater detail, and hence will be valuable to the Chief Administrator and the Coordinating Committee in reviewing the existing transportation program in terms of the total work that must be done and the personnel and skills needed for sound performance.

Coordination of Functions

From this brief review of the basic functions it is evident that they are intimately related, that all are part and parcel of transportation management, and that none can be conducted by itself in a vacuum. Moreover, it will be apparent that the quality of performance of the individual functions hinges on the degree of coordination in the administrative structure.

Ideally, these transportation functions should be combined into one department in order to achieve top efficiency at the operating level and to carry out effectively a comprehensive transportation planning program. In practice, however, it may not be feasible to merge all transportation activities in a single agency, especially when transit is either privately owned or operated by a special authority. In such cases, the force of the restrictions on achieving a balanced transportation program should be weighed.

Then, too, consolidation must be deliberated with regard to its effect on existing departments and personnel arrangements. In some communities, the engineering staff has responsibilities in addition to those in the transportation field. With this situation, it may not be easy to transfer personnel to a consolidated department. Again, such limitations should be considered in terms of effect on the planning, construction, and operation of the transportation system.

But regardless of local conditions, evaluating the existing status by means of an administrative study will help to determine the extent to which such consolidation is feasible and the form it should take—a new department, an enlarged department of public works, or some other solution.

Even where it is impossible to bring together

all the transportation functions, the establishment of a Technical Coordinating Committee of the type recommended in Stage I should go far toward achieving the sort of integration required. Such a committee, actively working as a team, can insure proper coordination not only of planning, but of construction, operations, and maintenance as well.

RELATIONS WITH OTHER JURISDICTIONS

Urban areas often encompass parts of two or three counties, several townships, and a half-dozen or more incorporated cities. Sometimes there also are large unincorporated "fringe areas." As far as local transportation is concerned, the entire area must be considered as an entity if headway is to be made in solving the many problems involved.

Absence of any coordinating or unifying force between local units of government has, in many instances, made it virtually impossible to deal adequately with transportation problems. This explains the diverse types and locations of signs, signals, and markings which so often are a source of confusion to the public. It explains why construction of urgently needed streets and highways is sometimes delayed because of conflicting ideas as to locations. Without some method of coordination between the various agencies involved, it will be difficult, if not impossible, to develop an integrated system of streets, highways, and transit service. The transportation plans of cities, towns, and unincorporated fringe areas must be in harmony and complement one another if metropolitan transportation needs are to be successfully met.

Subject to local circumstances and conditions, the traditional devices which may be used in a metropolitan area to integrate the planning and operation of street, traffic, and transit activities are: (1) extraterritorial controls, (2) annexation, (3) special authorities or districts, (4) intergovernmental agreements, (5) metropolitan planning agencies, and (6) various forms of consolidation of municipal and county government.

Many metropolitan areas are now giving serious attention to this problem. Some are conducting cooperative studies to decide what kind of areawide approach will best meet their needs. A few already have set up areawide authorities.

Today it is also imperative for a community to have close working relations with county, state, and federal agencies. Coordination, again, can be accomplished through the Technical Coordinating Committee, as recommended in Stage I. When matters of broad policy are involved, the City Councils of several cities in the area can resolve them in consultation with the County Board of Supervisors and state highway officials.

A sound organizational framework does not in itself constitute a guarantee of good administration, but with it competent management becomes easier to attain. There have been instances where good government has been achieved in spite of complicated, decentralized, or unwieldy structure and restrictive laws. The history of municipal government proves, however, that in general cities favored with a form of organization characterized by clear lines of authority and responsibility, and unfettered by inadequate laws, have made the greatest progress in improving operations.

MODERNIZING LAWS AND ORDINANCES

Cities must fact the fact that the demands of modern urban transportation require modern legal machinery. Because municipal officials can act only within the limitations of the law, they must have up-to-date legal authority if they are to carry out immediate and long-term objectives effectively.

Until now, few studies have been made to appraise the adequacy of urban transportation laws in relation to today's critical traffic needs. As a result, many officials have been unaware of legal deficiencies in their own fields until recently, when confronted with legal roadblocks in trying to launch an accelerated highway program. To the degree that this predicament exists, urban transportation progress will continue to be seriously, and unnecessarily, hampered.

Correcting this situation is a joint responsibility of the administrators involved, the City Attorney's office, and the legislative body. The administrators concerned must first determine and make known their legislative needs; the City Attorney, as legal officer of the city, must work in close cooperation with each official to translate those needs accurately into proper legal language, in accordance with state requirements; and finally, the City Council must consider and act on the proposals made.

Before these steps can be begun, the existing status of the law must be carefully evaluated. To help cities make the appraisal, there has been developed, in connection with this Guide, a manual which brings together the legal tools considered essential for the development of a sound urban transportation program. While prepared for the information and guidance of all officials with urban transportation duties under the law, the legal tools manual has been designed especially for the City Attorney, upon whom rests the responsibility of drafting or approving the language and form of all proposals submitted for Council action.

In the manual are assembled in outline form the law and its substantive elements—local, state, and federal—affecting the main administrative, engineering, and financial aspects of urban transportation.

To facilitate its use, the manual has been organized into five major sections: (1) planning, (2) construction of facilities, including right-of-way acquisition and financing, (3) control of their use, (4) enforcement, and (5) metropolitan and regional authorities. The basic laws relating to each of these broad categories are listed, with the principal elements of each briefly described.

The material is based on recommended legislative models, where they exist; the best state enabling acts, city charters, and ordinances known to be in effect; and, in the absence of such specific legal guides, authoritative reference documents dealing with the legal phases of the subject.

Up-to-date legal authority is needed for the job of modernizing urban transportation. A Legal Tools Manual has been developed as a guide to models of the best laws and ordinances now in effect, as well as to other authoritative reference materials dealing with the administrative, engineering, and financial aspects of the problem.

Planning

Under the group of planning laws, for example, are listed such legal instruments as those related to the development of the city's master plan, zoning, subdivisions, mapped streets, urban renewal, and civil defense.

As for the master plan, it can help materially to minimize future traffic problems since it provides a guide for the harmonious development of land and transportation facilities. A good master plan law also encourages effective integration of transportation and terminal facilities with other urban improvements, thus fostering sound community progress.

The model master plan act cited in the manual provides, among other things, for adoption of the plan by Council action. Some cities in recent years have found it advantageous to give the plan official status upon its approval by the Planning Commission, thereby obviating the need for legislative sanction whenever the plan is refined.

Zoning regulations control the location and density of traffic generators and hence are often effective in reducing traffic congestion. A zoning ordinance can influence the trend of real estate development so as to insure better use of street facilities. For example, it can encourage construction of apartment houses along transit routes, and thereby perhaps stave off overcrowding by private passenger cars. It can control erection of business establishments on major arterials, and in this way prevent excessive traffic generation.

To a greater extent than in the past, zoning ordinances today embody special provisions dealing specifically with traffic problems and related land-use development. They include, for example, requirements for the provision of off-street parking and loading and unloading spaces when new buildings are constructed or major renovations take place; for the screening of parking areas from adjacent residential developments to preserve the residential atmosphere; and for the location of terminal facilities in relation to the major street system.

Another strong ally of urban transportation planning is the subdivision law which requires developers to dedicate street rights of way and lay out street patterns in conformance with the master street plan.

Like other controls in this field, subdivision regulations stem from the city's police power and must be based on reasonableness. Generally, the courts have been liberal in their interpretation of what constitutes reasonable control of new subdivision design. This attitude recognizes that the community has a responsibility to develop an orderly plan for future traffic needs.

To avoid future obstacles to long-range street improvement plans, cities can use—in addition to subdivision control—the so-called "mapped street" authority. Under this legal instrument, municipalities can protect their plans for future streets or street widening by regulating the building of structures in the bed of mapped streets designated on the official map established by the Council. Enabling legislation for such authority has been enacted in most states.

With federal funds available to assist cities in urban renewal and civil defense programs, communities engaged in this work have an excellent opportunity to articulate these efforts with their transportation plans. This may require new or additional legal authority at both the state and local levels.

Provision of Facilities

Another group of basic laws bearing on urban transportation deals with such important activities as financing, land acquisition, and construction and maintenance.

Sound fiscal policies are prerequisite to the development of an efficient transportation system. Since the methods employed in financing transportation improvements have their foundation in law, the legal tools manual covers the different types of taxes levied for transportation purposes, methods of borrowing funds, authority for joint financing with other units of government, the financing of self-liquidating and self-supporting facilities, and other fiscal programs that can be utilized to provide for needed facilities.

In light of the stepped-up Federal Highway Program which requires communities and states to acquire a considerable amount of right of way in urban areas, the power to facilitate the acquisition of land has become of first-rank importance.

In many cases, right of way acquisition laws are obsolete in terms of today's needs and must be brought up to date if the new highway program is not to be burdened with excessive costs and delays. In metropolitan areas where several jurisdictions may be involved, special arrangements will have to be made to coordinate acquisition of needed right of way so that construction can proceed expeditiously. More than likely, state enabling legislation will be required.

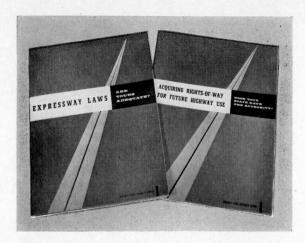

Adequate laws may be a big factor in getting the expanded Federal Highway Program completed on time. Control of access and advance acquisition of right of way are two of the important legal aspects which concern cities and metropolitan areas.

Where necessary, consideration should be given to providing authority to acquire property within and without corporate limits, for other jurisdictions, for future use, and for controlled access facilities. Similarly, legal revision may be necessary to authorize immediate possession, acquire marginal land, obtain land by reclamation, exchange property, and permit the right of entry to make surveys.

Legal provisions governing construction and maintenance pertain to such structures as streets, bridges, tunnels, expressways, parkways, freeways, and off-street parking and bus and truck terminal facilities.

Carrying out these activities may involve authority to cooperate with the state and other governmental units; adoption of design and construction standards; use of contract or force account methods in performing the work; and purchase and lease of equipment—all matters which should be clearly provided for in the law.

Traffic Control

More and more cities are achieving better use of their existing street facilities through traffic engineering measures. These operational techniques invariably serve to improve transportation in terms both of safety and of efficiency.

Full use of the resources of modern traffic engineering is largely dependent upon adequate enabling legislation. It would seem incumbent upon every city—in view of the great backlog of street improvements needed in urban areas—to make certain it has adequate authority for utilizing existing facilities to the best advantage.

This authority covers such matters as installation and maintenance of signs and signals, speed regulations, on-street and off-street parking controls, designation of one-way streets, through streets, stop streets, yield-right-of-way streets, truck routing, loading zones, pedestrian controls, and other regulations designed for more effective traffic control.

Many of these operational changes can be made administratively under broad powers, but such measures as parking prohibitions and establishment of one-way streets generally require specific legal authority through Council action.

An example of a regulation which can be effected by administrative discretion is speed zoning—though a change in the established speed limit must be warranted on the basis of traffic and engineering determinations. But in this, as in many other phases of local traffic control, state enabling legislation also may be required.

To touch upon related areas, appropriate authority for the issuance of licenses and permits can be an important factor in insuring conformance with the city's zoning plan and subdivision regulations and in controlling special uses of the transportation system. Included here are such items as building permits, permits for curb-cuts and utility installations, franchises for private and municipally-owned transit, and licensing of taxicabs and commercial parking facilities.

Studies made in many cities have shown that one of the most important underlying causes of transportation inefficiencies is diffusion of traffic control authority. Over the years responsibilities and duties in the municipal traffic field have been scattered haphazardly among numerous departments, divisions, and agencies. This diffusion often leads to duplication of effort, waste, and delay in urgently needed programs.

The root cause of this widely prevalent diffusion lies, as a rule, in the basic law. Much of the legislation now in force dates back to horse-and-buggy days. As a number of progressive cities have demonstrated, revamping of these outmoded laws is the first step toward proper consolidation and coordination of essential traffic functions.

Enforcement

Like traffic engineering, enforcement plays a leading role in the operation of urban street systems. In fact, enforcement is the other arm in the regulation of traffic. Proper coordination of the two is imperative if a maximum degree of safe, orderly, and unimpeded transportation service is to be afforded to the public.

Traffic police provide the needed flexibility of control which cannot always be built into devices or obtained through engineering measures alone. Adequate authority, therefore, must be provided for these operational functions, as well as for the apprehension and prosecution of traffic law violators. Moreover, sound judicial procedures must be established for the prompt and equitable disposition of all cases.

Communities which have made most progress in raising the level of police traffic administration have generally patterned the authority exercised on nationally recognized models which are cited in the manual.

With reference to the responsibility of the municipal court in transportation matters, the manual also lists, among other things, the essential elements of authority governing use of the nonfixable uniform traffic ticket; establishment of a traffic violations bureau; and cooperation with the state motor vehicle agency with regard to suspension and revocation of drivers' licenses. Pertinent recommendations for the improvement of the court system, as proposed by the Conference of Chief Justices, are also included.

Metropolitan Areas

The importance of areawide thinking and planning in handling transportation problems has been brought out in an earlier section of this Guide. Successful coordination between cities in a metropolitan area hinges on state enabling legislation. Such powers pertain to regional planning, creation of metropolitan transit or transportation authorities, intergovernmental agreements, annexation of fringe areas, extraterritorial zoning, consolidation of jurisdictions, and so forth.

Legal Tools Manual

The elements contained in the manual and briefly discussed here cover transportation in its broadest scope and for that reason may, in some particulars, go beyond the needs of some municipalities. Nevertheless, the manual can be very useful to cities of all population groups in measuring the adequacy of their legal authority in relation to modern transportation needs. It also can serve as a handy reference document to meet legislative requirements arising in the future. Kept up to date, it likewise will provide a continuing inventory of all municipal law on urban transportation.

Each municipality, it should be recognized, will have to consider this material in light of the special legal requirements of its own state. It also should be pointed out that the models, laws, and documents cited are by no means exhaustive, and that in some cases gaps exist. The National Committee is continuing efforts to furnish additional guides and to improve and refine the reference material listed.

Study Procedure

As has been stated previously, the City Attorney, as a key member of the Coordinating Committee, will actively participate in the deliberations on every phase of the program outlined in this Guide.

It is highly desirable that, as early as possible, he review with the Committee members individually those portions of the manual that relate to the responsibilities of each member. Since these officials bear the chief responsibility in all phases of municipal transportation, and are familiar with its problems, this cooperative approach is best calculated to reveal any inadequacies that may exist in the existing laws.

By the same token, the City Attorney should keep himself fully apprised of the plans and programs which the Coordinating Committee is developing during Stages III and IV so as to determine such legal changes as may be necessary. When the over-all plan is completed by the Coordinating Committee, it will be his responsibility (again with the advice of the other Committee members) to draft the legal documents to implement it. After approval of the plan by the Council, the legislation can be put in final shape.

As the program unfolds, new problems may arise which can be met only through additional legislation. To meet these situations, the City Attorney will find continuing guidance in the legal tools manual.

Procedure Manuals designed to be used in connection with *Better Transportation for Your City* may be obtained from Public Administration Service, 1313 East Sixtieth Street, Chicago 37, Illinois.

All recipients of this Guide will be advised of the availability of these Manuals as they are published.

CREDITS

INDEX

M

Maintenance
    cost accounting, 30, 31
    cost estimates, 67, 68
    project priorities, 77-79
Major Arterial Streets—*see* Arterial Streets, Major
Maps
    accident location, 21
    street classification, 42
    street inventory, 27-29
    street use, 12-14, 34
    traffic volume, 34
    transit routes, 23, 24
    travel desires, 32, 33, 53-55
Metropolitan Planning, 8, 85, 89
Modernizing Laws and Ordinances—*see* Laws and Ordinances
Motor Vehicle Accidents—*see* Accidents, Motor Vehicle

O

Off-Street Parking, 21, 50, 55
Origin-Destination Survey
    analysis of data, 32-34
    cost, 16-18
    data collection methods, 15, 16
    data projection, 39-42
    frequency of study, 16
    supporting data, 14, 16, 39-41
Organizing for the Job
    appointment of director, 6
    citizens' advisory committee, 6, 8, 9
    legislative approval, 6
    technical coordinating committee, 6, 7

P

Parking
    plans, 50
    studies, 21
    standards, 49, 50
Passenger, Transit
    loading study, 24
    origin-destination, 14, 15, 32, 36
    standards for loading, 51
    terminal facilities, 49, 50, 55
Pedestrian Service, 49
Planning Program
    city, 7, 56, 57
    metropolitan, 8, 85
Preliminary Plans—*see* Alternative Plans

Procedure Manuals
    use of, 3
Projecting Future Travel, 39-42
Project Priorities, 77-79
Public Information
    developing citizen interest, 8-10, 73-75
    public acceptance of plan, 3, 73-75

R

Records
    accidents, 20, 21
    financial, 29-31, 38, 39
    physical street system, 28, 29
    traffic control devices, 21, 22
    transit routes, 24
    see also Studies, Transportation
Revenues
    additional sources, 68-72
    inventory, 30, 31
    projection, 37-39, 68
Route Inventory, Transit, 24
Routes and Coverage, Transit, 23, 24

S

Schedules, Transit, 51, 52
Standards, Transportation
    street services and facilities, 42-46
    transit services and facilities, 51-52
Staggered Work Hours, 62
State Aid—*see* Aid, Federal and State
Streets
    capacity, 19, 20
    classification, 42-46
    geometric design, 50
    operational characteristics, 46-48
    structural condition, 27-29, 37, 49, 65
Street Systems
    criteria for establishing, 42-46
    evaluation of street service, 46-49
    study of street use, 12-14
Studies, Transportation
    administration, 81-85
    financial records, 29-31
    land use, 16
    laws and ordinances, 86-89
    origin-destination, 14-18
    physical street inventory, 27-29
    street use, 12-14
    traffic service: accidents, 20, 21; capacity, 19, 20; inventory of control devices, 21, 22; parking, 21; traffic volume, 18, 19; travel time, 19

transit service: frequency and regularity, 24-26; general operating data, 26, 27; loading, 24; riding habits, 27; routes and coverage, 23, 24; route inventory, 24; running time, 26; speeds and delays, 26

Subdivision Regulations, 87

Support Groups, Public, 9, 10, 73-76

T

Technical Coordinating Committee
    functions, 6, 7
    membership, 6, 7

Terminal Facilities
    parking: curb, 21, 49, 50, 55; off-street, 21, 49, 50, 55
    transit, 49, 50, 55
    truck, 49, 50, 55

Traffic Law Enforcement, 88, 89

Traffic Service and Facilities—*see* Studies, Transportation, *and* Standards, Transportation

Traffic Volumes
    determination, 18, 19
    projection, 39-42
    see also Origin-Destination Survey *and* Studies, Transportation

Transit Service and Facilities, 22-27
    see also Studies, Transportation *and* Standards, Transportation

Transportation Plan, 56, 57, 72, 73

Transportation Planning Program
    adopting the preferred plan, 73-76
    carrying out the plan, 77-80
    defining the problem, 32-55
    developing the transportation plan, 56-72
    getting the transportation facts, 11-31
    organizing for the job, 6-10

Transportation Standards—*see* Standards, Transportation

Transportation Studies—*see* Studies, Transportation

Travel Desires—*see* Origin-Destination Survey

Travel Speed
    auto, 19, 47-49, 53
    transit, 26, 52, 55

Truck
    loading zones, 49, 50, 55
    terminals, 50, 55
    travel—*see* Origin-Destination Survey

U

Urban Renewal, 1, 56, 62, 63

User Revenues, 68-70

W

Work Program, 79

Work Hours, Staggered, 62

Z

Zoning, 87